The Indepe...dent...
Guid...
UK and Ireland

Edited
by
Sam Dalley

One of a series of
guides for outdoor
enthusiasts and budget
travellers

The Backpackers Press

ISBN 0 9523381 4 9

The Independent Hostel Guide 1996:UK and Ireland

5th Edition

Edited by: Sam Dalley

British Library Cataloguing in Publication Data
A Catalogue record for this book is available from
the British Library
ISBN 0 9523381 4 9

Published by: The Backpackers Press, 2 Rockview
Cottages, Matlock Bath, Derbyshire, DE4 3PG,
Tel/Fax: (01629) 580427

© The Backpackers Press, 1996

Printed by: Echo Press, Loughborough
Cover Photography : Adam Chattaway

Distributed by:
            Cordee Books and Maps
            3a De Montfort Street
            Leicester, LE1 7HD
            Tel: (0116) 2543579

INDEPENDENT HOSTELS
WHAT ARE THEY ?

The Independent Hostels of the UK and Ireland vary from camping barns on the moors to lively backpackers hostels in historic cities, but they all offer a home from home atmosphere where cooking and living areas are shared. Some hostels have private rooms but most provide bunk accommodation in dorms and often require the use of a sleeping bag. Kitchens may be available, but at some hostels home cooked meals are a speciality or there is an attached pub for a pie and a pint. The hostels are all privately run and totally individual, there is no membership required and few rules or curfews. To find out more delve into this guide where the hostel descriptions will entice you to visit.

SYMBOLS

Mixed dormitories

Single sex dormitories

Private rooms

Blankets or Duvets provided

Sheets required

Sheets required - can be hired

Sleeping bags required

Sleeping bags required - can be hired

Hostel fully heated

Common room heated

Drying room available

Hot water available

Showers available

Cooking facilities available

Shop at hostel

Meals provided at hostel (with notice)

Breakfast only at hostel (with notice)

Meals available locally

ENGLAND

	Pg	Phone
Whitesand's Lodge, Land's End Backpackers, Sennen, Cornwall, TR19 7AR	9	(01736) 871776
Kelynack Bunkbarn, Kelynack, St Just, Penzance, Cornwall, TR19 7RE	10	(01736) 787633
Newquay Backpackers, Towan Beach, Newquay, Cornwall, TR7 1DR	11	(01637) 874668
Plymouth Backpackers, 172 Citadel Road, The Hoe, Plymouth, PL1 3BD	12	(01752) 225158
Plume of Feathers Bunkhouse, Princetown, Yelverton, Devon, PL20 6QG	13	(01822) 890240
Pixies Holt, Dartmeet, Yelverton, Devon, PL20 6SG	14	(01364) 631248
Dartmoor Expedition Centre, Rowden, Widecombe-in-the-Moor, Devon, TQ13 7TX	15	(01364) 621249
Southsea Lodge, 4 Florence Rd, Southsea, Portsmouth, Hampshire, PO5 2NE	16	(01705) 832495
Brighton Backpackers, 75/76 Middle Street, Brighton, BN1 1AL	17	(01273) 777717
Littlehampton Bunkhouse, 14 Pier Road, Littlehampton, Sussex, BN17 5BA	18	(01903) 715766
Kipps, 40 Nunnery Fields, Canterbury, Kent, CT1 3JT	19	(01227) 786121
Astor Hostels (Head Office), London	20	(0171) 2297866
Tent City Acton, Old Oak Common Lane, East Acton, London, W3 7DP	21	(0181) 7435708
Tent City Hackney, Millfields Road, Hackney, London, E5 0AR	22	(0181) 9857656

	Pg	Phone
Bath Backpackers, 13 Pierrepont Street, Bath, BA1 1LA	23	(01225) 446787
Oxford Backpackers, 9a Hythe Bridge Street, Oxford, OX1 2EW	24	(01865) 721761
Twenty Three, 23 Alvin Street, Gloucester, Gloucestershire, GL1 3EH	25	(01452) 418152
Alpheton Hostel, Monks' Croft, Bury Road, Alpheton, Sudbury, Suffolk, CO10 9BP	26	(01284) 828297
Stokes Bunkhouse, Newtown House Farm, Much Wenlock, Shropshire, TF13 6DB	.	(01952) 727293
Richard's International Hostel, 157 Wanlip Lane, Birstall, Leicester, LE4 4GL	27	(0116) 2673107
Tunstall Camping Barn, Tunstall, Halvergate, Norwich, Norfolk, NR13 3PS	28	(01493) 700279
The Old Red Lion, Bailey Street, Castle Acre, Norfolk, PE32 2AG	29	(01760) 755557
Courtyard Farm Bunkhouse, Ringstead, Hunstanton, Norfolk, PE36 5LQ	30	(01485) 525369
Deepdale Granary Bunkhouse, Burnham Deepdale, Norfolk, PE31 8DD	31	(01485) 210256
The Igloo Tourist Hostel, 110 Mansfield Road, Nottingham, NG1 3HL	32	(0115) 9475250
Forest Farm Bunkhouse, Mount Road, Marsden, Huddersfield, HD7 6NN	33	(01484) 842687
York Youth Hotel, 11/13 Bishophill Senior, York, YO1 1EF	34	(01904) 625904
The Barnstead, Stacksteads Farm, Ingleton, Carnforth, Lancashire, LA6 3HS	35	(015242) 41386
Timberlodge, Pinecroft, Ingleton, Carnforth, Lancashire, LA6 3DP	36	(015242) 41462
West View, Thornton-in-Lonsdale, Ingleton, Carnforth, Lancashire, LA6 3PJ	.	(015242) 41624
The Knoll, Horton-in-Ribblesdale, Settle, Nr Skipton, North Yorkshire, BD24 0HD	37	(01729) 860283
Dub-cote Bunkhouse, Three Peaks, Horton-in-Ribblesdale, North Yorks, BD24 0ET	.	(01729) 860238

	Pg	Phone
The Confluence Centre, Northcote, Kilnsey, Skipton, BD23 5PT	.	(01756) 753525
Skirfare Bridge Dales Barn, Northcote, Kilnsey, Skipton, BD23 5PT	.	(01756) 752465
Hill Top Farm Bunkbarn, Malham, Nr Skipton, North Yorkshire	.	(01729) 830320
Cam Bunkbarn, Cam Houses, Oughtershaw, Skipton, North Yorkshire, BD23 5JT	.	(0860) 648045
Punch Bowl Inn, Low Row, Swaledale, Richmond, North Yorkshire, DL11 6PF	.	(01748) 886233
Bents Camping Barn, Newbiggin-on-Lune, Kirkby Stephen, Cumbria, CA17 4NX	.	(015396) 23681
Lake District Backpackers, High Street, Windermere, Cumbria, LA23 1AF	38	(015394) 46374
Sticklebarn Bunkhouse, Sticklebarn Tavern, Great Langdale, Cumbria, LA22 9JU	39	(015394) 37356
Sykeside Bunkhouse, Brotherswater, Patterdale, Penrith, Cumbria, CA11 0NZ	40	(017684) 82239
Howtown Outdoor Centre, Howtown, Ullswater, Cumbria, CA10 2ND	41	(01768) 486508
Clove Lodge Camping Barn, Baldersdale, Barnard Castle, Co Durham, DL12 9UP	42	(01833) 650030
YMCA Weardale House, Ireshopeburn, Bishop Aukland, Co Durham, DL13 1HB	43	(0800) 591527
High Loaning Head Adventure, Garrigill, Alston, Cumbria, CA9 3EY	44	(01434) 381929
Bent Rigg Farm, Ravenscar, Scarborough, North Yorkshire	.	(01723) 870475
Harbour Grange, Spital Bridge, Whitby, North Yorkshire	.	(01947) 600817
Joiners Shop Bunkhouse, Preston, Chathill, Northumberland, NE67 5ES	.	(01665) 589245

8

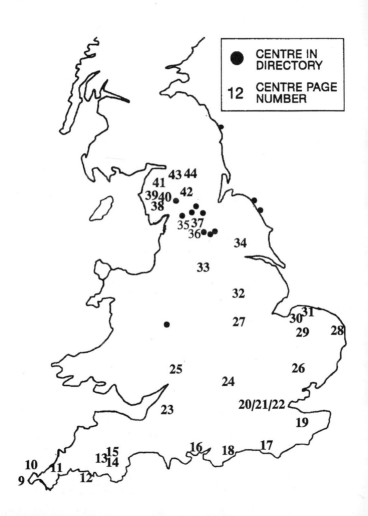

WHITESAND'S LODGE

Land's End Backpackers
Sennen
Cornwall
TR19 7AR

Whitesand's Lodge, a converted granite farmhouse, is situated in Cornwall's natural rugged beauty, surrounded by sea, cliffs, hills, walkways and wildlife. There are two types of accommodation, the dormitories with self catering kitchen for groups and backpackers, and the guest house, with more comfort, for couples and families. The general facilities are used by everyone. These include a cosy TV/Video lounge, a library, a residents bar and a cafe providing good cheap wholesome food all day.

Whitesand's Lodge provide a very exciting location for outdoor activities: from surfing, rock climbing, mountain biking and hiking the coastal paths to bird watching and retracing the area's ancient history. This is a great place for young and adventurous people from all over the world to have fun, to be challenged and to relax on one of Britain's most enchanting areas.

TELEPHONE CONTACT Toby (01736) 871776
OPENING SEASON All year
OPENING HOURS Open all day, no curfews.
NUMBER OF BEDS 30 in backpackers, 12 in guest house.
BOOKING REQUIREMENTS Groups should book.
PRICE PER NIGHT £8 (backpackers dorms), £12.50 (guest house). Group packages discussed. Full breakfast from £2.50.

DIRECTIONS The hostel is first left as you enter Sennen Village on A30. 9 miles from Penzance (phone for pick up from Penzance train/bus terminal). 1½ miles from Land's End and 5 mins walk from beach and coastal path.

KELYNACK BUNKBARN

Kelynack Camping Park
Kelynack, St Just
Penzance, Cornwall
TR19 7RE

Kelynack Bunkbarn nestles in the secluded Cot Valley, one mile from the Atlantic Coast in the heart of the Lands End Peninsula area of outstanding natural beauty. The Barn has two twin rooms, one two bedded and one four bedded bunkroom. Blankets and pillows are provided. A communal kitchen with full cooking facilities is available without meters. Adjacent is the bike store and a laundry/drying room shared with the campers on site. A small shop on site opens between April and September.

St Just, a mile away has plenty of food shops, some banks and a selection of pubs and eating houses. Kelynack is ideal for coast and moorland walking, spending time on the beaches, birdwatching, rock climbing and exploring the ancient villages, standing stones and tin mining heritage of unspoilt West Penwith.

TELEPHONE CONTACT Jenny Edwards (01736) 787633
OPENING SEASON All year
OPENING HOURS Arrive after 2pm and vacate by 10am. All day access during stay.
NUMBER OF BEDS 10
BOOKING REQUIREMENTS Booking is advised (25% deposit).
PRICE PER NIGHT £5 adult, £3 child (under 12). No meters.

DIRECTIONS GR 373 301. The hostel is 200 yards west of the B3306, 1 mile south of St Just, 5 miles north of Lands End and 20 mins walk from the coastal path. Frequent bus from Penzance Rail Station to St Just.

NEWQUAY CORNWALL BACKPACKERS

International Hostel
Towan Beach
Newquay
Cornwall
TR7 1DR

Newquay is the surfing capital of the UK on the rugged North Cornwall coast, with the finest coastline and beaches in Europe. This hostel offers low cost accommodation in the heart of Newquay for surfers and overseas travellers. Overlooking Newquays best surf beaches we offer dorm style accommodation and twin rooms. We have a kitchen, hot showers, sauna, TV/video lounge, surf videos and great music. We also have board storage, security lockers and no curfews. A great base for surfing the many beaches, pubbing, clubbing, raging and even working (no maximum length of stay), alternatively mountain bike the Cornish coast or horse ride though the sand dunes. *Surfers and overseas travellers only.*

TELEPHONE CONTACT Manager (01637) 874668
OPENING SEASON All year
OPENING HOURS 24 Hours
NUMBER OF BEDS 25
BOOKING REQUIREMENTS Groups must book, individuals normally ok. No group bookings from May to Sept.
PRICE PER NIGHT £4 - £6.50 depending on season. Weekly discount rate of £39 (Apr-Sept) and £28 (Oct-Mar).

DIRECTIONS From bus/train station walk towards town centre. Turn right at pedestrian mall into Beachfield Ave. The hostel is 50 metres on the left. Driving into Newquay follow signs for town centre. At Towan beach turn right into Beachfield Avenue.

PLYMOUTH BACKPACKERS INTERNATIONAL HOSTEL

172 Citadel Road
The Hoe
Plymouth
PL1 3BD

Plymouth Backpackers is located just five minutes walk from the ferry port, where boats leave for Roscoff and Santander on most days. The hostel is close to all amenities, being a few minutes walk from the famous Barbican, Mayflower Steps and city centre. Also near to the bus and railway stations. Excursions to Dartmoor, canoeing on the Tamar River, sailing and walking the coastal paths can be arranged from plymouth.

We have 2,4 and 8 bedded dorms, linen is included in the price. There is a fully equipped kitchen and a TV lounge. A residents bar will be open by the summer with good sound!

TELEPHONE CONTACT (01752) 225158
OPENING SEASON All year
OPENING HOURS No curfew, all day access.
NUMBER OF BEDS 48
BOOKING REQUIREMENTS Booking is not essential but is preferred.
PRICE PER NIGHT £7.50 per person

DIRECTIONS From train station walk up Salt Ash Road to North Croft roundabout. Turn right along Western Approach to Pavilions. From bus station walk up Exeter Street, across roundabout to Royal Parade. Cross road to Union Street, Pavilions on your left. From Plymouth Pavilions walk towards the Hoe, turn left up Citadel Road, the hostel is in 100yds on the right hand side. Phone for a courtesy car.

THE PLUME OF FEATHERS INN BUNKHOUSE

Princetown
Yelverton
Devon
PL20 6QG

The Plume of Feathers Inn is situated in the moorland village of Princetown which is the main village in Dartmoor National Park. The park covers 365 square miles and is famous for its rugged beauty, quaint villages, prehistoric remains, and its many peaks, such as High Willhays (2039ft) and Yes Tor (2030ft). The Plume is a traditional family run Inn dating from 1785, it has log fires, real ale and plenty of atmosphere. The Alpine bunkhouse and New bunkhouse provide comfortable low cost accommodation and the Inn also has B&B accommodation and a 75 tent camping area with toilets and showers. There is a wide range of activities available in the Dartmoor area including: - sailing, fishing, riding, abseiling, white water canoeing, climbing, pony trekking and walking.

TELEPHONE CONTACT (01822) 890240
OPENING SEASON All year
OPENING HOURS All Day
NUMBER OF BEDS 42
BOOKING REQUIREMENTS To secure beds book in advance with 50% deposit. Booking three to four months in advance may be required for weekends.
PRICE PER NIGHT From £2.50 to £5.50 per person.

DIRECTIONS The Plume of Feathers Inn is on the edge of Princetown village square, in the centre of Dartmoor.

Pixies Holt

Residential Centre
Dartmeet, Yelverton, Devon
PL20 6SG
Tel: 01364 631248

What do you do in the School Holidays?
At Pixies Holt we have some vacancies during the school holidays. We can therefore offer the following facilities to an organised group wanting to sample Dartmoor's delights during the school holidays or the December-February period.
Please note: Group bookings only (with sole use of the Centre).

- a warm and welcoming atmosphere
- comfortable accommodation for groups of 17-35 people in a range of small rooms
- large common room
- separate dining room
- boots, waterproofs, etc
- good wholesome food (freeing organisers from the tasks of buying, preparing, cooking and washing up - packed lunches available)

Charges: (1.4.95 - 31.3.96)
(ALL MEALS INCLUDED)
£16.40 per person per night
Fee reductions for groups larger than 25

DARTMOOR EXPEDITION CENTRE

Rowden
Widecombe-in-the-Moor
Newton Abbot
Devon, TQ13 7TX

Why not come to Dartmoor to try walking, climbing, canoeing, caving and stay at the Dartmoor Expedition Centre. Two 300 year old barns with their cobbled floors and thick granite walls have been converted into basic but comfortable bunk-house accommodation. Downstairs in The House Barn there is a living and cooking area with everything needed for self catering including two Calor stoves (each with four rings, oven and grill) and a sink with a gas water heater. Upstairs there is a dormitory with bunk beds for nine and a small inner room with another five beds. The Gate Barn is used for sleeping only and there are eleven bunk-beds downstairs and a further nine upstairs. Both barns have night storage heaters and metered power points. Each bed is provided with a pillow, a pillowcase and a blanket.

TELEPHONE CONTACT John Earle (01364) 621249.
OPENING SEASON All year
OPENING HOURS 7.30am to 10.30pm
NUMBER OF BEDS 32
BOOKING REQUIREMENTS Book as far in advance as possible with 25% deposit.
PRICE PER NIGHT £5.50 per person per night.

DIRECTIONS GR 700 764. Come down Widecombe Hill into the village. Turn right 200yds after school and travel up a steep hill past Southcombe onto the open moor. Continue for one mile until you reach crossroads. Turn right and take first left after 400 yds. Hostel is 200yds on left.

SOUTHSEA LODGE

4 Florence Road
Southsea, Portsmouth
Hampshire
PO5 2NE

Portsmouth is one of Britains major tourist resorts and only island city. It offers a unique blend of seaside resort and historical navel heritage area containing, HMS Victory, The Mary Rose and Warrior ships. Southsea Lodge is almost directly opposite the Pyramid Centre Water Park on Southseas attractive Seafront, 5 mins walk from a major shopping precinct, and an excellent variety of pubs, clubs and eating places. Train Station and Port within 2 miles, with ferry services to France, Spain and the Islè of Wight. The Lodge offers travellers a warm welcome in a friendly relaxed atmosphere. Accommodation is in small dorms and doubles, some with en-suite facilities. There are spacious dining/social areas with TV/Video, pool table, well fitted kitchens and bathrooms and a patio garden with Barbecue. Secure cycle store and car parking available.

TELEPHONE CONTACT Pete/Margaret (01705)832495/822963
OPENING SEASON All year, 365 days
OPENING HOURS 24hr access, service 7.30am to 11.30pm
NUMBER OF BEDS 45
BOOKING REQUIREMENTS Booking is not essential, but advisable in high season. Deposit secures bed.
PRICE PER NIGHT £8 (small dorms) £10 (twin/double), £11 (twin/double en-suite)

DIRECTIONS From station, bus and ferry terminal follow directions to Sea Front and Pyramid Water Park. 50m east of Pyramids, follow footpath through gardens to Florence Rd. Or take bus to The Strand (junction of Waverley and Clarendon Rds) walk west, Florence Rd is the third turning on the left.

BRIGHTON BACKPACKERS INDEPENDENT HOSTEL

75/76 Middle Street
Brighton
BN1 1AL

Brighton, sometimes known as 'the small London by the sea' is action packed, especially in the summer. The historic cobbled lanes burst with life and the large student population provide lots of performing street artists. There are more night clubs per head of population than anywhere else in Britain. **Brighton Backpackers** is placed bang in the middle of this and only 50 metres from the central beach. It is a fun packed crazy place for international travellers with a relaxed and friendly atmosphere. Internally it has painted murals and cartoon characters, social areas with good Hi-Fi, satellite television and pool table, great for meeting other travellers. In addition to the dormitories Brighton Backpackers has double rooms with en-suite bathrooms and sea views. No curfews - all modern facilities including laundry.

TELEPHONE CONTACT (01273) 777717
OPENING SEASON All year
OPENING HOURS 9am to very late.
NUMBER OF BEDS 50
BOOKING REQUIREMENTS Advised to confirm beds.
PRICE PER NIGHT £9.00 per person. Special weekly rate.

DIRECTIONS From train station:- walk (10 mins) straight to the seafront (Kings Road), turn left and then left again into Middle Street, hostel is 20 metres up on the right hand side.

LITTLEHAMPTON BUNKHOUSE

14 Pier Road
Littlehampton
Sussex, BN17 5BA

Littlehampton on the mouth of the river Arun is a commercial and pleasure port, a centre for all water sports. It is the headquarters for many sea anglers championships and a popular centre for divers with more then 100 wrecks to explore. West of the river is a large expanse of unspoilt beach. About 3 miles away is Arundel with its castle, wildfowl and wetland area. The South Downs Way, a favourite route for walkers and cyclists, passes through Arundel. Nearby is Chichester with its cathedral and festival. There are also country homes to view at Goodwood, Petworth, Parkham and at Bignor and Fishbourne there are Roman remains.

The bunkhouse, a converted boat house, is 50 yards from the river and public slipway and a few minutes walk from the town centre and beach. There are self catering facilities and a snack bar just around the corner. Clean sheets are provided and there are 2 rooms with 12 and 4 bunks. Electricity is metered.

TELEPHONE CONTACT Mrs Henry (01903) 715766
OPENING SEASON All year
OPENING HOURS By appointment, no curfew.
NUMBER OF BEDS 16
BOOKING REQUIREMENTS Booking (one month in advance with 25% deposit) is recommended during summer.
PRICE PER NIGHT £6 per person.

DIRECTIONS From **Train Station** turn left at cross roads and walk 4 mins to the right to Pier Road. By **car** follow signs to beach, turn right, follow right bend into Pier Road. Parking just before white house (No 14).

KiPPS
40 Nunnery Fields
Canterbury
Kent
CT1 3JT

KiPPS is a 5-10 minute walk from the city centre of historic Canterbury with its renowned cathedral and top quality shops - a destination for pilgrims ancient and modern! Canterbury also makes an ideal stop over to start and finish a continental tour with easy access to the channel ports of Dover and Ramsgate. Everyone is welcome to enjoy the friendly relaxed atmosphere, whether travelling as an individual, family or group. Accommodation varies from 6 bedded dormitories to twin and single rooms. Also available are family rooms where cots can be provided. The small hostel shop offers breakfast and snack items and can also provide the ingredients for a simple but filling meal. For the adventurous caterer and those who have left more than their tooth brush behind a major supermarket is less than 10 minutes walk away. Smoking is prohibited within the house.

TELEPHONE CONTACT David Harman (01227) 786121
OPENING SEASON All year
OPENING HOURS No Curfew
NUMBER OF BEDS 40
BOOKING REQUIREMENTS Advance booking recommended 10% (minimum £5) deposit required to secure reservations.
PRICE PER NIGHT £9.95 to £12.95. Discounts available for longer stays and groups. Credit cards accepted.

DIRECTIONS Take B2068 to Hythe from City Ring Road (A28). Turn right at first traffic lights by church. KiPPS is 200-300 yds on left.

TENT CITY - ACTON
Old Oak Common Lane
East Acton
London
W3 7DP

Tent City Acton is a place where a tourist can spend a night in London at a very reasonable price. The accommodation is in bunk beds in large marquee tents. There are mens, womens and mixed tents and the main building has free hot showers and toilets, free cooking facilities and cheap nourishing meals. There is an on-site shop and snack bar and laundry and ironing facilities.

The hostels is open all summer, 24 hours a day with no curfew, and London Transport buses run close to the site all night. We also provide free baggage and valuable storage, helpful volunteer staff and a relaxed and friendly environment. There are volley ball and football pitches on-site and there is plenty of room for travellers with their own tents.

TELEPHONE CONTACT Reception (0181) 7435708
OPENING SEASON June 1st to Sept 7th inclusive
OPENING HOURS 24 hours
NUMBER OF BEDS 270
BOOKING REQUIREMENTS Booking is only required for groups of more then 10 people. No deposit needed.
PRICE PER NIGHT £5.50 per person, discounts for group bookings and extended stays.

DIRECTIONS Take the central Line London Underground train to East Acton. Tent City is 5 minutes walk from the station, where there is a map. All-night bus N23 runs close to the hostel from Trafalger Square.

TENT CITY - HACKNEY

Millfields Road
Hackney
London
E5 0AR

Tent City Hackney is a lovely cannal-side campsite and tented hostel in the heart of the Lea Valley nature reserve. Amazingly Tent city is also close to the City of London. The accommodation is in bunk beds in large marque tents and in small dome tents. The main building has free hot showers and toilets, free cooking facilities and cheep nourishing meals. There is an on-site shop and snack bar and laundry and ironing facilities. We are open all summer, 24 hours a day with no curfew. We also provide free baggage and valuable storage helpful volunteer staff and a relaxed and friendly environment. There is a childrens play area, on-site entertainment and local canal-side pubs. There is plenty of room for travellers with their own tents.

We believe that we are the cheapest accommodation in London.

TELEPHONE CONTACT Reception (0181) 9857656
OPENING SEASON June 1st to Sept 7th inclusive
OPENING HOURS 24 hours
NUMBER OF BEDS 100
BOOKING REQUIREMENTS Booking is only required for groups of more then 10 people. No deposit needed.
PRICE PER NIGHT £5.00 per person, discounts for group bookings and extended stays.

DIRECTIONS Liverpool Street underground then take 22a bus to Millfields Road, walk over the humpback bridge to the tented hostel. All-night buses N38 amd N96 run from Trafalger Sq.

BATH BACKPACKERS HOSTEL

13 Pierrepont Street
Bath
BA1 1LA

The closest hostel to Bath's railway and bus station. Centrally located to all amenities and shops and close to all historic sites.

During the week, there are organised walking tours around the area, taking in the River Avon and town centre.

Bath Backpackers is an historic Georgian building that is over 200 years old. It is the only independent hostel in Bath with a self catering kitchen, social room, smoking den, pool table and our awesome sound system throughout the hostel and shower rooms.

Bath Backpackers is a totally fun packed place to stay for international travellers. No curfews.

TELEPHONE CONTACT (01225) 446787 Michelle / Sue / Kiwi Dave
OPENING SEASON All year
OPENING HOURS 24 hr access, service 9am to 12 midnight
NUMBER OF BEDS 60
BOOKING REQUIREMENTS Booking is advised
PRICE PER NIGHT £8 per person

DIRECTIONS From Bath railway station:- walk straight out of the entrance and follow Manvers Street, 200m past bus station, Manvers Street runs into Pierrepont Street. Bath Backpackers hostel is on the left. From Bus station, follow route above.

OXFORD BACKPACKERS

9a Hythe Bridge Street
Oxford
OX1 2EW

Oxford Backpackers is a purpose built hostel, newly opened in the heart of Oxford the leading University town of England. The hostel is two minutes walk from the train and bus stations and close to the Tourist Information Centre and all the city's attractions. It is safe, clean and friendly and there are no chores or curfews. Fully equipped kitchen, games room and organised activities add to the experience. Small friendly dorms and two private rooms.

Oxford City is steeped in history and culture, you can explore Christ Church, Magdalen and New College of the University, Bodleian Library, the Oxford Story and Britain's oldest museum the Ashmolean Museum. Alternatively explore the canals and quiet villages of the Cotswolds.

TELEPHONE CONTACT Brent Smith (01865) 721761
OPENING SEASON All year
OPENING HOURS Access from 8am to 12 midnight.
NUMBER OF BEDS 80
BOOKING REQUIREMENTS During the summer (April to Sept) booking is required 7 days in advance with deposit by credit card.
PRICE PER NIGHT £9.00 per person

DIRECTIONS 100yds from Oxford train station. From station turn left, at fork bear left and hostel is on your right. From Oxford coach station turn right, hostel is over the bridge 100 yards on your left.

"TWENTY THREE"

23 Alvin Street
Gloucester
GL1 3EH

Despite international acclaim we are still a small, cosy and friendly family run hostel. Bed linen, duvets, pillows, hot showers, towels and central heating are all inclusive. No curfew, no extra charges, no smoking. We have laundry facilities, a secure and dry cycle store and a resident cycle mechanic. Cycle hire and guides available.

Within five minutes walk of the bus and train stations close to tourist information, restaurants, pubs, shops, culture and the old port of Gloucester. Overlooking the cathedral, resting place of the murdered King Edward. Surrounded by the beautiful Severn Valley flood plain, bordered by the Cotswold hills and the ancient Forest of Dean. A walkers, cyclists and hostellers paradise.

TELEPHONE CONTACT Jill (01452) 418152
OPENING SEASON All year
OPENING HOURS Flexible
NUMBER OF BEDS 6
BOOKING REQUIREMENTS It's best to telephone (sorry about the answerphone). Bookings are only required for groups. One months notice and 50% deposit.
PRICE PER NIGHT £7.50 or £50 per week (7 days).

DIRECTIONS GR 836 189. Five minutes walk from bus/train stations. From Gloucester Cross follow Northgate Street until it becomes London Road. Alvin Street is on the left after the Q8 petrol station.

ALPHETON
INDEPENDENT HOSTEL
Monks' Croft, Bury Road
Alpheton, Sudbury
Suffolk, CO10 9BP

Monks' Croft, the small hostel at Alpheton, offers simple accommodation for country-goers. The countryside is gently undulating, cycling country with quiet lanes and picturesque villages. Based at Alpheton you can ride out to these places and also to Constable Country. Cyclists, ramblers, school groups, Duke of Edinburgh's Award Scheme participants and children's organisations are welcome. Minium age is 5 years. Facilities are basic. The single storey hostel has two dormitories with a total of 19 beds. In addition there is a 9 bed annexe. No meals are provided. However there is a small hostel store and a large kitchen for self-catering. Bread and fresh milk should be ordered in advance.

TELEPHONE CONTACT Vic Copsey (01284) 828297
OPENING SEASON 1st April until 31st October
OPENING HOURS No access from 10am to 5pm. Please arrive before 10.30pm on first night.
NUMBER OF BEDS 19 plus 9 in annexe
BOOKING REQUIREMENTS Booking is strongly advised. Individuals please pay full cost when booking. Groups please pay 20% on booking and balance 1 month prior to visit. Please make cheques payable to V.H.Copsey.
PRICE PER NIGHT Child £3, Adult £5.50. Reductions for children's groups (leaflet available).

DIRECTIONS GR 882 511. The hostel is situated on the A134 between Sudbury (7 miles) and Bury St.Edmunds (9 miles). Limited bus service by Felix Taxis (01787) 310574

RICHARD'S INTERNATIONAL BACKPACKERS HOSTEL

157 Wanlip Lane
Birstall
Leicester, LE4 4GL

Richard's Place caters for backpackers, cyclists (on the Dover to Inverness cycleway) and other young tourists. This small warm hostel is a suburban home opened up to offer a you a welcome and a feast. Included in the nightly price is bedding, hot showers and as many cups of tea and coffee as you can drink. Richard specialises in large, home cooked meals (vegetarian and vegan if required). Also home baked bread and cakes. Breakfast (60p to £2.50), supper (£2.50 to £4.00) and large filled baps from 60p. The larger meal prices are for Richard's 'as much as you can eat' mega meals and he personally guarantees that if anyone can still eat after one meal he'll give them another one for free. In summer time a chalet house (no beds) is available for guests with their own bedding roll. Tent space also available. No Smoking.

TELEPHONE CONTACT Richard (0116) 2673107
OPENING SEASON All year
OPENING HOURS No access from 9am to 5pm. Open before 5pm in bad weather.
NUMBER OF BEDS 10 (including chalet)
BOOKING REQUIREMENTS Phone to book a bed. Answer phone service before 5pm.
PRICE PER NIGHT £8 first night, £7 thereafter or £40 per week. £3.00 per night in chalet house and tent space.

DIRECTIONS   Frequent bus service from Leicesters St Margaret's bus station (stand B) Bus No 2 or 125 (ask for Windmill Ave). Birstall is 3 miles north of Leicester on the A6. In Birstall look for the Somerfield store on Wanlip Lane.

TUNSTALL CAMPING BARN

Manor Farm
Tunstall
Halvergate
Norwich
Norfolk, NR13 3PS

Tunstall Barn is near the Great Yarmouth end of the Weavers Way Long Distance footpath, which is a 56 mile walk between Cromer on the North Norfolk Coast and Great Yarmouth on the East Coast. The barn is on the edge of Halvergate Marshes, one of the newest national parks, which is in the heart of Broadland. The barn is ideally situated for walkers and people involved in activities on the broads, rivers or coast. We can help to organise activities such as sailing, canoeing, cycling, horse riding and bird watching. The barn consists of sleeping platforms, a food preparation room with cooking equipment and hot water, a shower and a toilet. There is plenty of space to sit outside on a paved area, with a large brick barbecue and an extensive grass area where tents can be pitched. Write, phone or fax for a leaflet.

TELEPHONE/FAX CONTACT Robert or Sally More (01493) 700279
OPENING SEASON All year
OPENING HOURS Open all day, keys collected by 7pm.
NUMBER OF BEDS 20
BOOKING REQUIREMENTS Minium of 24 hours notice is required. Block bookings require a deposit 7 days in advance.
PRICE PER NIGHT £3.50 per person. Groups of 10+ £3.

DIRECTIONS GR 409 089. Turn off A47 between Acle and Great Yarmouth at the sign to Halvergate. From Halvergate follow signs to Tunstall. The Manor house is on the left before the ruin of Tunstall Church.

THE OLD RED LION
Bailey Street
Castle Acre
Norfolk PE32 2AG

Visitors to Castle Acre are entranced by the special atmosphere of this medieval walled town which lies within the outer bailey of an 11th century castle. Castle Acre is on the Peddars Way, an historic long distance path. The Old Red Lion, a former pub is centrally situated and now carries on the tradition of serving travellers who seek restoration and repose. Guests can stay in private rooms or dormitories where bedding and linen are provided free of charge. There are quiet areas with wood burning stoves for reading and meeting other guests and playing. There are two large areas (one self contained with catering facilities and toilets) which are ideal for group use, courses and retreats. The self catering facilities are suitable for groups and communally served meals (wholefood) are available. The entire premises are available for hire. Secure bike store. The Old Red Lion is NO SMOKING throughout.

TELEPHONE CONTACT Alison Loughlin (01760) 755557
OPENING SEASON All year
OPENING HOURS Free time, by prior negotiation.
NUMBER OF BEDS 18
BOOKING REQUIREMENTS Useful but not essential.
PRICE PER NIGHT With full bedding and breakfast from £10.

DIRECTIONS GR 818 151. Castle Acre is 3½ miles north of Swaffham on the A47. The Old Red Lion is situated on the left 75 yards down Bailey Street (go under Norman Arch in village centre). Call at the back. Buses to Castle Acre, from Swaffham three times a week and from King's Lynn two times a week. British rail stations at King's Lyne and Downham Market. Daily national express coach between Victoria and Swaffham.

COURTYARD FARM
BUNKHOUSE BARN
Ringstead
Hunstanton
Norfolk, PE36 5LQ

The Bunkhouse Barn was converted from a cattle shed in 1986 and the original character of the building has been preserved. There are two bunkrooms containing 4 and 8 bunks, toilets, sinks and showers are provided with metered hot water. The common room has tables, benches and a cooking area with metered electric kettle and hob. There are limited drying facilities on hooks over an electric heater and some car parking. You will need to bring :- a sleeping bag, plenty of 10p's and all cooking utensils (cutlery, plates, pans, washing up liquid).

The nearby Norfolk Coast features miles of sandy beaches and fascinating nature reserves. The Peddars Way long distance path is also easily accessible from the farm. There are some lovely circular walks on the farm lands and Ringstead Common is an ideal spot for a picnic. Courtyard Farm is ideal for walkers, bird watchers and lovers of the countryside.

TELEPHONE CONTACT Janet Calvert (01485) 525369
OPENING SEASON All year
OPENING HOURS 24 hours
NUMBER OF BEDS 12
BOOKING REQUIREMENTS Booking is not essential but the bunkhouse is often fully booked.
PRICE PER NIGHT £4 per person.

DIRECTIONS The farm is signposted 1.2 miles from Ringstead on the Docking road. Nearest rail station is King's Lynn (15 miles), buses run regularly between King's Lynn and Hunstanton (4 miles) but only 2 daily buses from Hunstanton to Ringstead.

DEEPDALE GRANARY BUNKHOUSE

Deepdale Farm
Burnham Deepdale
Norfolk, PE31 8DD

Deepdale Granary Bunkhouse is the ideal base for exploring the unique Norfolk Coast. It is situated halfway between Hunstanton and Wells-Next-The-Sea on the A149.

The hostel has modern facilities including central heating and hot showers. It also has a good self-catering kitchen.

Phone or fax anytime for a fully descriptive leaflet.

TELEPHONE/FAX CONTACT Alister Borthwick Tel (01485) 210256 Fax (01485) 210158
OPENING SEASON All Year
OPENING HOURS All day (collect key from office).
NUMBER OF BEDS 18
BOOKING REQUIREMENTS Pre-booking strongly recommended. 20% deposit with balance due one month in advance.
PRICE PER NIGHT £6.50 per person. £5.75 per person (weekdays) if all 18 beds are booked.

DIRECTIONS GR 803 443. On the A149 halfway between Hunstanton and Wells-Next-The-Sea, situated beside a garage.

THE IGLOO
TOURIST HOSTEL
110 Mansfield Road
Nottingham
NG1 3HL

Located within walking distance of the city's historical sights and entertaining sounds, the Igloo is Nottingham's only tourist hostel. On offer to backpackers and youth groups is a clean, safe and warm overnight stay in a large listed Victorian house. Just £8 per night per person buys a whole host of homely comforts:- bunk bed dorms, hot showers, TV lounge and fully-equipped kitchen plus free tea, coffee and good company. An optional self serve, eat-as-much-as-you-like breakfast is available for £2. Open in outlook and open all day all year, the Igloo is the ideal home-from-home for hostellers seeking rest and recuperation before pursuing the exploits of local hero, Robin Hood, or enjoying the nightlife of this popular university city.

TELEPHONE CONTACT Steve (0115) 9475250
OPENING SEASON All year
OPENING HOURS Open all day. 3am curfew.
NUMBER OF BEDS 23
BOOKING REQUIREMENTS Not essential, but advised for groups. Confirm large group booking in writing (deposit may be required).
PRICE PER NIGHT £8 per person

DIRECTIONS From the Tourist Information Centre, Market Square, Nottingham. Turn right out of T.I.C, take the next left onto Clumber Street and keep walking straight on for ten minutes until you reach the Golden Fleece Pub. The Igloo is diagonally opposite the Pub.

FOREST FARM BUNKHOUSE

Mount Road
Marsden
Huddersfield
West Yorkshire
HD7 6NN

Forest Farm Bunkhouse is a traditional handloom weaver's farmhouse over 300 years old. It has been restored to provide self catering accommodation for up to 19 people and keeps many aspects of its original character. The bunkhouse has a fully equipped kitchen, two shower rooms, drying facilities and central heating. There is a small shop on site and meals and pack lunches can be provided. Bedding can be provided on request.

The bunkhouse is situated on the edge of the village of Marsden, 1000ft above sea level, enjoying views of the Pennine Hills and Peak District. It is a convenient stopping place for walkers on the Pennine Way (400 metres away), mid-way between Crowden and Mankinholes Youth Hostels. Local activities include walking, rock climbing, riding, windsurfing and mountain biking.

TELEPHONE CONTACT (01484) 842684
OPENING SEASON All year
OPENING HOURS Flexible
NUMBER OF BEDS 19
BOOKING REQUIREMENTS Booking is essential, book as early as possible with 50% deposit.
PRICE PER NIGHT £6.50 per bed. Weekend exclusive use £110 per night. Mid Week exclusive use £100 per night.

DIRECTIONS GR 041 104. Mount road is opposite the golf club in Marsden, Which is half way between Huddersfield and Oldham, just off A62. The Pennine Way is 400 metres away.

THE BARNSTEAD

Stacksteads Farm
Ingleton
Carnforth
Lancs. LA6 3HS

The Barnstead is situated in the beautiful Yorkshire Dales, one mile from Ingleton village centre. It has panoramic views of Ingleborough and Whernside, and is within easy access to the Lake District and Lancashire coast. We provide bunk-style self-catering accommodation, in two separate units, for individuals, families or groups. Local attractions include rambling, fell walking, pot-holing, climbing and geological and historic sites. Both units are centrally heated, sleeping bag liners, duvets and pillows are provided, inclusive of price. Unit One has:- 22 beds in 4 dorms, large lounge/dining area, drying room, large fitted kitchen (with cookers, fridges, freezers, crockery and utensils) and male & female washrooms with showers. Unit Two has:- One 6 bed dorm, kitchen/lounge and washroom with shower. No extras. Tourist Board Inspected with full N.I.C.E.I.C certificate.

TELEPHONE CONTACT Mona/Jim Charlton (015242) 41386
OPENING SEASON All year
OPENING HOURS 24 hours
NUMBER OF BEDS (Unit 1) 22 beds (Unit 2) 6 beds.
BOOKING REQUIREMENTS Pre-booking advised with as much notice as possible. Deposit required.
PRICE PER NIGHT (Unit 1) £7 per person or £120 for exclusive use. (Unit 2) £7 per person (minimum of 4).

DIRECTIONS GR 686 724. On main A65 Kirkby Lonsdale to Settle road. When travelling south turn right at Masons Arms pub in Ingleton. In 300 yards turn right into farm. Nearest train station (Bentham) 3 miles. Nearest buses (Ingleton) 1 mile.

TIMBERLODGE
Pinecroft, Ingleton
Carnforth, Lancashire
LA6 3DP

Timberlodge is a Scandinavian pine lodge for self catering groups or individuals, situated half a mile from Ingleton on the edge of the Yorkshire Dales. The surrounding limestone landscape is renowned for its excellent underground systems. The famous Gaping Ghyll system is popular with cavers and for the those that like to keep dry there are show caves featuring stalagmites, stalactites and a massive 200,000 year old ice age cavern. The three Peaks Race route is accessible to the enthusiastic walker and from Ingleton there is a pleasant four miles walk on maintained footpaths through spectacular waterfall and woodland scenery.

The lodge is fully double glazed and centrally heated. It has spacious bunkrooms for 2 to 6 people, hot showers, sauna, and an excellent drying room. The kitchen is well equipped with gas and electric cookers, dishwasher, fridge freezer, microwave and a food warmer which will hold 48 meals. The large dining room has a soft drinks machine and satellite television and video. There is a payphone for incoming/outgoing calls (015242) 42119.

TELEPHONE CONTACT Robin and Dorothy Hainsworth (015242) 41462
OPENING SEASON All year
OPENING HOURS 24 Hours
NUMBER OF BEDS 48
BOOKING REQUIREMENTS Booking (with deposit) is advised with as much notice as possible, particularly for groups.
PRICE PER NIGHT £7 per person. Exclusive use available.

DIRECTIONS GR 699719, The hostel is ¾ of a mile south of Ingleton on the A65

THE KNOLL

Horton-in-Ribblesdale
Settle
Near Skipton
North Yorkshire
BD24 0HD

This Victorian house appeals to the independent hosteller by virtue of its superb location, yards from the Pennine Way footpath. The Knoll is situated in an acre of its own grounds in the centre of Horton-in-Ribblesdale village. There is a village store at the bottom of the grounds, the railway station is five minutes walk away and the house is midway between two pubs, neither of which is more than two minutes walk.

The sleeping accommodation is in private rooms with blankets and linen provided. The rooms are large and comfortable with central heating, colour television and tea making facilities. A good home made breakfast is included in the price and there is a drying room and cycle store ideal for the outdoor enthusiast. A large Victorian conservatory acts as a common area where you can relax with views of the village pub, church and hills. There are good views of Pen-y-Ghent and Ingleborough as the Knoll is situated on top of a small hill.

TELEPHONE CONTACT Sylvia Ireton (01729) 860283
OPENING SEASON All year
OPENING HOURS All day
NUMBER OF BEDS 4 Double and 2 single.
BOOKING REQUIREMENTS Booking is advised (£5 deposit)
PRICE PER NIGHT £12 per person.

DIRECTIONS Next door to the post office midway between the two pubs in Horton-in-Ribblesdale.

LAKE DISTRICT
BACKPACKERS LODGE
High Street
Windermere
LA3 1AF

One of the most beautiful parts of England and very famous for its poet William Wordsworth and Beatrix Potter. Windermere is a small town on the edge of Lake Windermere - England's largest lake.

Lake District Backpackers is opposite the Tourist Information Centre, bus station and railway station. Its a totally relaxed place to stay and save your sanity. One of the friendliest hostels in England. It offers free tea and coffee at your convenience, Saturday night BBQ's and water-skiing in summer; great pubs and close to all amenities. Lake District Backpackers is halfway between London and Scotland.

A place that can't be missed if you are in the area.

TELEPHONE CONTACT Sue, Michelle, Kiwi Dave (015394) 46374
OPENING SEASON All year
OPENING HOURS 9am to 10pm (winter), 9am to 12 midnight (summer).
NUMBER OF BEDS 32
BOOKING REQUIREMENTS Booking is advised
PRICE PER NIGHT From £8 per person

DIRECTIONS From train and bus station walk out of station car park, past supermarket, down to Tourist Information Centre. Walk across the street to the National Westminster Bank and follow pavement down 5m and we are right there.

STICKLEBARN BUNKHOUSE

Sticklebarn Tavern
Great Langdale
Cumbria
LA22 9JU

The Sticklebarn is beautifully situated amidst some of the finest mountain scenery in England. It is at the very foot of the famous Langdale Pikes and Dungeon Ghyll waterfalls and seven miles north west of Ambleside. The Sticklebarn is unique to Lakeland as it is privately owned and is available to the general outdoor public and traveller on foot. The bunkhouse has no common room or self catering facilities but there is a T.V room and meals service provided in the pub. Sorry no pets. A brochure is available on request.

TELEPHONE CONTACT Peter Ingham (015394) 37356
OPENING SEASON All year
OPENING HOURS Open all day. Food served all day, breakfasts available between 8.00am and 10.30am.
NUMBER OF BEDS Winter 21, Summer 18
BOOKING REQUIREMENTS Pre-booking is advised for weekends and groups (at least 7 days in advance) and requires a deposit or booking form.
PRICE PER NIGHT £8.00 per person.

DIRECTIONS From the A591 Windermere to Keswick road at Ambleside take the A593 turn to Coniston / Torver. After two miles take the B5343 to Great Langdale via Chapel Stile. The Bunkhouse is adjacent to the Sticklebarn Tavern. Bus service 516 to Great Langdale from Ambleside, ask for Old Dungeon Ghyll Hotel, walk 5 mins (phone (01946) 632222 for timetable).

SYKESIDE BUNKHOUSE

Skyeside Camping Park and Brotherswater Inn
Sykeside, Brotherswater, Patterdale
Penrith, Cumbria, CA11 0NZ

Sykeside Bunkhouse accommodation is open throughout the year and is situated in the heart of the mountains in the Dovedale Valley with unique views all around. It is ideally situated for walking and climbing and is a good base for touring the Lake District. The local stone built bunkhouse is adjacent to the campsite, well off the main road. It consists of several rooms each sleeping between 2 and 6 persons in pine bunk beds. The rooms are carpeted and heated, and each bed comes equipped with bottom sheet, blanket, pillow and pillow case. A limited number of sleeping bags are available for hire from the site shop. There is an indoor area where you may cook (bring your own stoves and utensils) or alternatively breakfasts and bar meals are available at 'The Barn End' bar and restaurant. The bunkhouse has full use of the campsite facilities including, toilets, showers, power points, hot water, dishwashing area, fully stocked shop, washing machines and driers. Accommodation is also available in the Brotherswater Inn.

TELEPHONE CONTACT (017684) 82239
OPENING SEASON All year
OPENING HOURS 24 hours
NUMBER OF BEDS 36 in bunkhouse + 25 in Inn
BOOKING REQUIREMENTS Telephone booking required, deposit of one nights payment should be sent within four days.
PRICE PER NIGHT £7.50(bunkhouse) £8.50(Inn) per person. Two nights minium stay is required for those staying on Fridays.

DIRECTIONS On the A592 Between Ullswater and the Kirkstone Pass. Park entrance is next to the Brotherwater Inn, approximately three miles south of Patterdale.

HOWTOWN OUTDOOR CENTRE

Howtown, Ullswater
Cumbria, CA10 2ND

Howtown Outdoor Centre was established in 1966 and offers top quality outdoor education courses and comfortable catered accommodation. Vegan and vegetarian options are available at meal times and the beds, for 30 females and 30 males, include duvets and bed linen. We mainly operate with groups although individuals are welcome when the centre is not booked for the sole use of a group. The centre overlooks Ullswater and is only 20 minutes from Penrith and the M6. The area is ideal for virtually every outdoor activity with its own foreshore and immediate access to the lakes and fells of the Lake District and the Coast to Coast Walk. Ullswater is England's most peaceful lake, it has a 10mph limit so sailing, windsurfing and canoeing are undisturbed by noise and wash. The wildlife is plentiful and varied. We provide courses, customised to your needs, in sailing, canoeing, windsurfing, rock climbing, abseiling, kayaking, hill walking, gully scrambling, skiing and orienteering.

TELEPHONE CONTACT (01768) 486508
OPENING SEASON All year (mainly weekends)
OPENING HOURS Access from 4pm till 10am. Daytime access can be arranged for groups.
NUMBER OF BEDS 60
BOOKING REQUIREMENTS Booking (deposit) is essential.
PRICE PER NIGHT £7 per person (bed only). Groups of 10+ £6 per person. Further reductions by negotiation for large groups.

DIRECTIONS From Pooley Bridge, follow the minor road on the east side of Ullswater, signposted Howtown and Martindale, for 3½ miles. Howtown steamer pier on the right, turn immediately left.

CLOVE LODGE
CAMPING BARN

Baldersdale
Barnard Castle
Co Durham
DL12 9UP

In an idyllic position, 1000ft up in the Northern Pennines at the head of beautiful Baldersdale, Clove Lodge offers shelter and comfort to those walking the Pennine Way. There is no need to make a detour as the camping barn is directly on route at the half way point. Anyone wishing to spend time walking or cycling in the beautiful, unspoilt countryside will find Clove Lodge an attractive base.

The accommodation, in a recently converted barn, is simple and rustic (nothing more than a stone tent) with wooden sleeping platforms plus cooking and sitting areas. The luxury of a hot shower and toilet are provided in an adjacent outbuilding. Basic provisions may be bought on site, and a hearty breakfast and farmhouse supper can be had in the converted stables tearoom. Self catering or B&B accommodation is also available.

TELEPHONE CONTACT Phil/Ann Heys (01833) 650030
OPENING SEASON From March 1996
OPENING HOURS Flexible by arrangement
NUMBER OF BEDS 12
BOOKING REQUIREMENTS Booking recommended
PRICE PER NIGHT From £4.50

DIRECTIONS GR 936 177 From Barnard Castle take B6277 to Cotherstone. Turn left just past the Fox and Hound Inn signposted Blackton & Hury Reservoirs. Fork left after 2 miles. Clove Lodge is a further 2 miles at the end of the road.

Y.M.C.A. WEARDALE HOUSE

Ireshopeburn
Bishop Aukland
Co Durham
DL13 1HB

Weardale House is situated in the North Pennine Hills, England's last wilderness, and uses the hills, crags, mines and rivers as natural ingredients in its outdoor activities programme. The centre is in the village of Ireshopeburn, some thirty miles from Durham City. It is in close proximity to Kilhope Wheel, Alston, Hexham, Middleton-in-Teesdale and High Force. We offer an optional outdoor activities programme, led by qualified staff and with all equipment provided. Activities include canoeing, climbing, abseiling, underground exploration, navigation, fell walking, orienteering and skiing. There are no self catering facilities but all meals are provided by the centres domestic staff.

TELEPHONE CONTACT Lesley Willis (0800) 591527
OPENING SEASON All year
OPENING HOURS All day
NUMBER OF BEDS 60
BOOKING REQUIREMENTS Booking (deposit) is essential.
PRICE PER NIGHT All prices include all meals. Phone for nightly rate. Weekend rates (2 nights), £40 or £46 with program of activities. Midweek rates (4 nights), £99 or £114 with program of activities.

DIRECTIONS The centre is one mile from St Johns Chapel on the A689 in Upper Weardale. The nearest rail station (30 miles) is Durham City on the East Coast Main Line. A public bus service operates up the dale (Weardale Coaches 01388 528235)

HIGH LOANING
HEAD ADVENTURE

Garrigill
Alston
Cumbria
CA9 3EY

Loaning Head Adventure is situated in Garrigill close to the border of Cumbria and Durham. The Pennine Way passes through the village as does the Coast to Coast Cycle Way. This family run centre has six bedrooms with bunks to sleep seventeen people, fully fitted kitchen, dining room, games room and drying room. Central heating, showers and all bedding is provided inclusive. Registered with the tourist board the centre is equipped to superior hostel standard. A self contained cottage on site offers additional or independent accommodation for up to ten.

In addition Lindsay Williams offers structured or informal courses using mountains, rivers, lakes and mines. The programmes are based upon :- personal resources through outdoor pursuits, individual and group effectiveness, democracy and community action, adventure and career development, cross curricular action learning, wilderness and rural aesthetics.

TELEPHONE CONTACT Lindsay (01434) 381929
OPENING SEASON All year
OPENING HOURS 24 Hours
NUMBER OF BEDS 27
BOOKING REQUIREMENTS Booking not required.
PRICE PER NIGHT £6 self catering, £15 full board.

DIRECTIONS GR 748 417. Loaning Head is signposted off the B6277 which follows Teesdale from the A1 though Barnard Castle and Middleton to Alston.

WALES

	Pg	Phone
Smithy's Bunkhouse, Lower House Farm, Pantygelli, Abergavenny, Gwent, NP7 7HR	47	(01873) 853432
Joe's Lodge, Hay Road, Talgarth, Nr Brecon, Powys, LD3 0AL	48	(01874) 711845
Trericket Mill Bunkhouse, Erwood, Builth Wells, Powys, LD2 3TQ	49	(01982) 560312
Caban Cwmffynnon, Cefn Gorwydd, Llangammarch Wells, Powys, LD4 4DW	50	(01591) 610638
Stonecroft Hostel, Dol-y-coed Road, Llanwrtyd Wells, Powys, LD5 4RA	51	(01591) 610332
Llysdinam Field Centre, Newbridge on Wye, Llandrindod Wells, Powys, LD1 6NB	.	(01597) 860308
Brithdir Mawr, Cilgwyn Road, Newport/Trefdraeth, Pembrokshire, SA42 0QJ	52	(01239) 820164
Y Beudy, Maes Y Morfa, Llangrannog, Llandysul, Dyfed, SA44 6RU	.	(01239) 654561
Canolfan Corris, Old School, Corris, Machynlleth, Powys, SY20 9QT	53	(01654) 761686
Caban Cader Idris, Islawrdref, Dolgellau, Gwynedd, LL40 1TS	54	(01341) 423178
Just Beds, Bryn-Teify, King Edward Street, Barmouth, Gwynedd, LL42 1PE	55	(01341) 281165
The Coach House, Tomen Y Castell, Llanfor, Bala, Gwynedd, LL23 7HD	.	(01678) 520738
Stone Barn, Tyddyn Morthwyl, Criccieth, Gwynedd	56	(01766) 522115
Old School Bunkhouse, Hen Ysgol, Bwlch Derwin, Pant Glas, Gwynedd, LL51 9EQ	57	(01286) 660701
Bryn Dinas Bunkhouse, Bryn Dinas, Nant Gwynant, Caernarfon, LL55 4NH	58	(01766) 890234
The Heights Hotel, 74 High Street, Llanberis, Gwynedd, LL55 4HB	59	(01286) 871179
Jesse James' Bunkhouse, Penisarwaen, Nr Llanberis, Gwynedd, LL55 3DA	60	(01286) 870521
Totters, Plas Porth Yr Adar, 2 High Street, Caernarfon, Gwynedd, LL55 1RN	61	(01286) 672963
Outdoor Alternative, Cerrig-yr-Adar, Rhoscolyn, Holyhead, Anglesey, LL65 2NQ	62	(01407) 860469

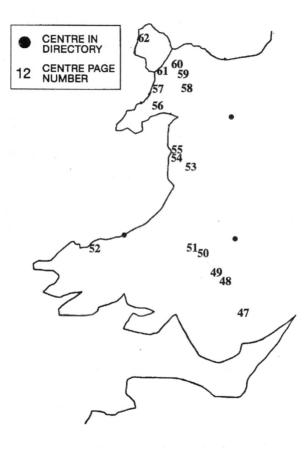

CENTRE IN DIRECTORY

12   CENTRE PAGE NUMBER

62

60
61   59
57   58
56

55
54
53

52

51 50

49
48

47

SMITHY'S BUNKHOUSE

Lower House Farm
Pantygelli
Abergavenny
Gwent, NP7 7HR

Located on a working hill farm, Smithy's Bunkhouse lies in the Black Mountains within the Brecon Beacons National Park, some two miles from the historic market town of Abergavenny. Designed to accommodate a maximum of 24 persons in two dormitories of 12 bunks, additional space is available above the common room if required. The bunkhouse is equipped with showers, toilets, fully equipped kitchen, drying area (with coin operated washer and dryer), public telephone and a common room with wood buring stove. It is heated during the winter by night storage heaters, hot water and electricity are supplied at no extra cost, some firewood is provided and extra may be purchased. A 16th century coaching Inn is located at the top of the farm drive which serves bar snacks, restaurant meals and traditional ales. The area is ideal for walking, climbing, caving, mountain biking, canoeing, water sports, pony trekking.

TELEPHONE/FAX CONTACT Neil or Katy Smith (01873) 853432 fax 850599
OPENING SEASON All year
OPENING HOURS 24 Hours by arrangement
NUMBER OF BEDS 24
BOOKING REQUIREMENTS Booking is advised with £50 deposit for groups. Cheques payable to Smithy's bunkhouse.
PRICE PER NIGHT £7 per person, Group bookings £6.

DIRECTIONS GR 304 178. Pantygelli village is located two miles north of Abergavenny just off the old Hereford Road. The bunkhouse is down the farm track opposite the Crown Inn.

JOE'S LODGE
Hay Road
Talgarth
Nr Brecon
Powys, LD3 0AL

Joe's Lodge is a family-run bunkhouse providing B&B, or for parties of 15 or more exclusive use self catering (B&B optional). Evening meals can be provided by arrangement, but there is plenty of good value pub grub (& real ale) nearby. Talgarth is a small market town at the foot of the Black Mountains with the Brecon Beacons 12 miles, Offas Dyke 7 miles and the Wye at Glasbury about 3 miles distant. It is ideally situated for the serious and not-so-serious walker. The river Wye offers canoeing, kayaking or white water rafting in the winter. Sailing and wind surfing is available on Llangorse Lake, and qualified instructors can be arranged for caving, abseiling and gorge walking. We have a drying room, Sky TV and parking space. Special family holidays are available during Aug with under 11's at half price.

TELEPHONE CONTACT Jason (01874) 711845
OPENING SEASON All year
OPENING HOURS By arrangement
NUMBER OF BEDS 27
BOOKING REQUIREMENTS No Later than one week in advance (longer for bank / half term holidays) with 10% deposit.
PRICE PER NIGHT £9.50 b&b, evening meal by arrangement. Groups of 15+ self catering £6.50 per person.

DIRECTIONS GR 155 340 (sheet 161). Talgarth is on A479 between Crickhowell and Bronllys. From market square, walk 150yds past MACE shop (on left), Joe's lodge is on left. British rail services to Abergavenny (18 miles away) or Hereford (20 miles). Good bus service from Hereford to Talgarth. Buses from Abergavenny on Tues and Thurs (phone for timetables).

TRERICKET MILL BUNKHOUSE
Erwood
Builth Wells
Powys
LD2 3TQ

Across the stream from Trericket Corn Mill this stone bunkhouse in an old cider orchard overlooks the river Wye. It is particularly suitable for small groups and individuals as there are two rooms sleeping four people each and an additional en suite bunkroom for two attached to the mill. The bunkhouse is clean and cosy with wood burning stoves. Hot water and showers are inclusive. Limited self catering facilities are provided in a covered outdoor kitchen. Alternatively breakfasts and packed lunches can be provided and good pub meals are available locally. There are heated drying and common rooms in the mill. Camping available.

Situated on the Wye Valley Walk this is an ideal stop over for walkers and for anyone wishing to spend time in the beautiful area of Mid Wales. Canoeing, riding, gliding and mountain bikes all available locally. Brochure on request.

TELEPHONE CONTACT Alistair/Nicky Legge (01982) 560312
OPENING SEASON All year
OPENING HOURS 24 hour access
NUMBER OF BEDS 8 (+ 2 in mill)
BOOKING REQUIREMENTS Booking advised.
PRICE PER NIGHT £7.50 per person. Sole occupancy (8) £50.

DIRECTIONS GR 112 414, OS sheet 148. We are set back from the A470 Brecon to Builth Wells road between the villages of Llyswen and Erwood. British Rail stations at Builth Wells, Cardiff and Hereford with daily bus service to Erwood.

CABAN CWMFFYNNON

Cefn Gorwydd
Llangammarch Wells
Powys
LD4 4DW

Situated in the Heart of Wales, Caban Cwmffynnon is a century old stone barn, converted into a comfortable bunkhouse. It is an ideal base for field studies, residential and management courses.

The Caban is easily accessible to the Brecon Beacons and the Elenydd Range of hills, and activities include hill walking, pony trekking, mountain biking and expedition training. It can be an ideal base for the many events held in nearby Llanwrtyd Wells. The Caban will also be on the new National North/South Cycle Route. Hill walks, guided walks and bird watching breaks can be organised through Dinefwr Treks for groups and individuals. BBQ area and limited camping available.

CABAN CWMFFYNNON   Escape to our beautiful landscapes

TELEPHONE CONTACT Bryan Jones (01591) 610638
OPENING SEASON All year
OPENING HOURS No access from 10am to 5pm.
NUMBER OF BEDS 24
BOOKING REQUIREMENTS Not essential. Deposit required.
PRICE PER NIGHT £7.50 (discounts for groups).

DIRECTIONS   GR 907 439 (Landranger map 147).   Three miles south east of Llanwrtyd Wells. Heart of Wales railway service to Llanwrtyd Wells (one hours walk to Caban) and Llangammarch Wells (40 mins walk to Caban).

STONECROFT HOSTEL

Dol-y-coed Road
Llanwrtyd Wells
Powys, LD5 4RA

Stonecroft Hostel town centre self catering guest house, is situated in Llanwrtyd Wells, "the smallest town in Britain". Surrounded by the green fields, mountains and glorious countryside of Mid Wales, Llanwrtyd is renowned as Red Kite country, and is central for mountain biking, pony trekking, walking, photography and bird watching. There are regular town events such as the "Man V Horse race" and guided walks and cycle hire are available. Stonecroft Hostel offers a comfortable stay and a warm Aussie welcome. We have central heating, showers, dormitories, private rooms, bed linen, fully equipped kitchen, dining area TV room, reading lounge, bike store, parking and a river side garden. The hostel is a home away from home, and next door is the Stonecroft Inn (featured in 1996 Good Beer Guide), a traditional country pub, where breakfasts, packed lunches and meals are always available.

TELEPHONE CONTACT Diane Lutman (01591) 610332
OPENING SEASON All year
OPENING HOURS Register between 9am and midnight in summer, or noon and midnight in winter. No curfew.
NUMBER OF BEDS 20 - 25
BOOKING REQUIREMENTS Welcome, but only essential for town event weekends. 50% deposit required.
PRICE PER NIGHT Private room:- £10 adults, £8 children. Dormitory:- £8 adults, £6 children. Long stay reductions and group discounts.

DIRECTIONS From A483 (Llandovery to Builth Wells) turn left at north side of bridge into Dol-y-coed Rd. Hostel is 100 yds on left next door to Stonecroft Inn.

BRITHDIR MAWR
Cilgwyn Road
Newport / Trefdraeth
Pembrokeshire
SA42 0QJ

Brithdir Mawr is a converted cow house with two sleeping lofts and a family room. It is run by a small community set up to steward a beautiful and partly wild piece of land. We aim to live simply on permaculture principles, using sustainable methods wherever possible. This includes 12 volt electricity from wind, water and sun.

Brithdir Mawr is just under the Preseli mountains. Newport, Pembrokshire is two miles away and is on the Pembrokeshire Coastal Path which stretches for 180 miles along cliffs and beaches.

We practise home education. Music, dance and movement plays a part, so does connection with spirit. We have a daily meditation. Visitors are welcome to join in any activity.

TELEPHONE CONTACT Julian or Emma Orbach
(01239) 820164
OPENING SEASON All year
OPENING HOURS All day
NUMBER OF BEDS 12
BOOKING REQUIREMENTS Always phone in advance.
PRICE PER NIGHT £4 per person

DIRECTIONS GR 074 373. Take road to Cilgwyn signposted from A487 Fishguard to Cardigan Road at the edge of Newport. Go 2km towards Cilgwyn and the hostel drive is on your left.

THE DYFI VALLEY

One of the greenest corners of Europe, in the heart of Mid Wales, the Dyfi Valley offers an unique holiday experience. It is centred on the ancient market town of **Machynlleth**, home of the last Welsh Parliament House and its prince, the legendary Owain Glyndŵr. Today the mysteries and magical world of the Celts can be discovered at **Celtica** and two miles up the narrow wooded valley is the world renowned **Centre for Alternative Technology**, with practical solutions for a world of green living. Also near the valley are nature reserves, sandy beaches and the mighty **Cader Idris** mountain. **Canolfan Corris** provides comfortable quality accommodation ideal for your visit. Catered or self catering options for choice and value. Open most of the year, see page 45, tel/fax Michael Parish (01654) 761686.

CABAN
CADER IDRIS
Islawrdref
Dolgellau
Gwynedd
LL40 1TS

Caban Cader Idris is a listed building in a secluded wooded valley within walking distance of Cader Idris and the Mawddach Estuary in Snowdonia National Park. It is in an ideal setting for field work and outdoor pursuits with wonderful unspoilt mountain, valley and estuary walks from the doorstep. Local activities include:- climbing, hill walking, pony trekking, biking, canoeing, rafting and fishing. The area is also ideal for the study of geology, geography, local history, industrial archaeology and ornithology (RSPB woods adjoin grounds). Nearby are slate mines, dry ski slope, narrow gauge railways and beaches. There is a large kitchen/dining room, two dorms sleeping 6 and 10, a lounge (with 3 beds), toilets, hot showers and a drying room. It is heated and has a payphone, car park and fire safety certificates. Camping by arrangement. Phone for a brochure.

TELEPHONE CONTACT (01248) 600478 / (01341) 423178
OPENING SEASON All year
OPENING HOURS No restrictions
NUMBER OF BEDS 19
BOOKING REQUIREMENTS Booking is essential with £10 per night deposit for groups. Last minute enquiries welcome.
PRICE PER NIGHT £6 per person. Sole use:- £60 per night week, £80 on Friday and Saturday.

DIRECTIONS GR 682 169. From Dolgellau take the A493 Fairbourne road on south of Mawddach estuary. One mile beyond Llynpenmaen/Penmaenpool take left hand turn just before Abergwynant Bridge. The bunkhouse is on left in 300 yds.

JUST BEDS, BRYN-TEIFY
King Edward Street
Barmouth
Gwynedd
LL42 1PE

Just Beds (Bryn-Teify) is a small Victorian residence with many original features. The TV and music lounge has a superb oak fireplace, delft shelf and fine cornicing. Accommodation is in double and twin rooms with bedding, sheets and towels provided free of charge. Facilities for making hot drinks and eating takeaways are available. Tea, coffee and milk are provided.

Barmouth is situated on the coast of Snowdonia on the River Mawddach estuary where the Cader Idris range of mountains roll down to the sea. The seafront and beach stretch for two miles on firm sand where swimming is safe and water standards high. The naturalist will love the colourful slopes of the estuary where oak woodland alternate with coniferous forest. Sheltered valleys are the home of a wealth of bird life and wild plants. The estuary is the haunt of wading birds and the heather-clad hills are the sanctuary of magnificent birds of prey. No Smoking in hostel.

TELEPHONE CONTACT Alan (01341) 281165
OPENING SEASON All year
OPENING HOURS Flexible (keys available)
NUMBER OF BEDS 6
BOOKING REQUIREMENTS Please phone. Prepaid booking only please.
PRICE PER NIGHT £9 per person. Long stay reduction.

DIRECTIONS Situated on the main road through Barmouth going north towards Harlech. Just Beds is near to the Roman Catholic church, next to a garden (locals will give directions). Barmouth has a British Rail service and bus service.

STONE BARN
Tyddyn Morthwyl
Criccieth
Gwynedd
North Wales

The Stone Barn is a converted farm building at Tyddyn Morthwyl Farm and Caravan Park near Criccieth on the fringe of Snowdonia. It provides a good centre for climbing and walking in Snowdonia and the Lleyn Peninsula. Tremadog Rocks (an all year rock climbing venue) is only 7 miles away. Canoeing and wind surfing nearby.

The barn has basic bunkhouse facilities with hot showers and toilets and laundry facilities shared with the caravan park. There is a wood burning stove for heating and clothes drying (wood provided free) and a kitchen area with fridge and running water. Several pubs in the locality serve good bar meals. There is additional sleeping accommodation for 4 ladies in a cedar wood chalet. Also static caravans and self catering cottages to let.

TELEPHONE CONTACT Mrs Trumper (01766) 522115
OPENING SEASON All year
OPENING HOURS Flexible
NUMBER OF BEDS 12 + 4 ladies in chalet
BOOKING REQUIREMENTS 48 hrs advanced booking required, with one nights fee as deposit.
PRICE PER NIGHT £4 per head inc wood (discount for 12 or more people).

DIRECTIONS 1¼ miles from Criccieth on B4411 Caernarfon road.

THE OLD SCHOOL BUNKHOUSE

Hen Ysgol
Bwlch Derwin
Pant Glas
Gwynedd
LL51 9EQ

Re-discover peace and quiet by exploring the newly-opened footpaths and bridle-ways which stretch from Snowdon to Bardsey Island along the spine of the Lleyn Peninsular. For climbers the crags of Tremadog, The Rivals and Cwm Silyn are close by.

The Old School Bunkhouse, standing in the grounds of an old school, and surrounded by forest, provides an ideal location for walkers, cyclists and all other out-door enthusiasts. The bunkhouse is well equipped for self catering but The Old School B&B can also provide delicious home-cooked meals and packed lunches by prior arrangement. Also available is a flat, sheltered camping field and ample off road parking.

TELEPHONE CONTACT Terry or Sue (01286) 660701
OPENING SEASON All year
OPENING HOURS All day
NUMBER OF BEDS 1 to 12
BOOKING REQUIREMENTS Booking is essential, 10% deposit required.
PRICE PER NIGHT £4.50 per person per night. £4.00 per person per night for groups of 5 plus.

DIRECTIONS GR 456 474. From the A487 Porthmadog to Caernarvon road turn at Pant Glas and follow the road for approx 1 mile. The Old School is on the left, set back from the road

BRYN DINAS BUNKHOUSE

Bryn Dinas
Nant Gwynant
Caernarfon
LL55 4NH

Bryn Dinas Bunkhouse / Hostel is situated in the magnificent Gwynant Valley right at the foot of Snowdon on the south side. The facilities are basic, adequate and clean. It has been run by Jerry and Barbara Rogers for thirty years. There is a good selection of pubs, cafes and restaurants in Beddgelert.

There are two grades of accommodation:-

- Twenty four bunk beds are arranged dormitory style in a traditional Welsh farm-house.
- Twenty six bunk beds are in wooden cabins of various sizes in the centre grounds.

The establishment is fully fitted out for self catering. Please write or ring for our descriptive leaflet.

TELEPHONE CONTACT Jerry/Barbara Rogers(01766) 890234
OPENING SEASON Open all year
OPENING HOURS Totally flexible
NUMBER OF BEDS 50
BOOKING REQUIREMENTS Advanced booking (with deposit) is recommended.
PRICE PER NIGHT From £5.95 per person.

DIRECTIONS GR 625 503. Situated in the Gwynant Valley at the foot of Snowdon. Three miles from the village of Beddgelert on the A498.

THE HEIGHTS HOTEL
74 High Street
Llanberis
Gwynedd
LL55 4HB

THE HEIGHTS HOTEL, LLANBERIS. The meeting place for climbers and mountaineers.

Ideally situated in the heart of Snowdonia.

Backpackers dormitory accommodation available for groups or individuals. £10.50 B&B or £7.50 bed only.

Facilities include bar, restaurant, video screen, music, pool room, and climbing wall

Rock climbing tuition available.

Open all year round.

TELEPHONE CONTACT (01286) 871179
OPENING SEASON All year
OPENING HOURS Access from 8am to 12 midnight
NUMBER OF BEDS 24
BOOKING REQUIREMENTS Booking is not essential, but recommended to save disappointment.
PRICE PER NIGHT £7.50(bed) or £10.50 (bed and breakfast) per person.

DIRECTIONS Situated in the centre of Llanberis, very easy to find.

JESSE JAMES' BUNKHOUSE

Penisarwaen
Nr Llanberis
Gwynedd
LL55 3DA

Snowdonia's Original Bunkhouse, going since 1966, a comfortable base for non-smoking outdoor people. Perfectly situated between the mountains and the sea, the area is ideal for walking, climbing, canoeing, cycling or just soaking up the peace. Hostel or flat to suit all tastes, home cooking or self catering - gas and microwave, fridge/freezer with all eating and cooking gear. Showers and drying room, private off-road parking and camping. Sleeping bags needed - yours or hire mine.

Do your own thing, or hire me, an MIAC mountain guide. Introductory navigation, climbing, abseiling, canoeing and sailing, available by arrangement. Mature adults welcome. This is a centre of Lo-Tech Pragmatism - keep it simple so long as it works. Here it does. Ring or write for a leaflet.

TELEPHONE CONTACT Jesse James (01286) 870521 24hrs
OPENING SEASON All year, but enquire first.
OPENING HOURS All day
NUMBER OF BEDS 38 in several grades
BOOKING REQUIREMENTS Book if possible, ring or write. 50% deposit for weekends, less for longer.
PRICE PER NIGHT From £6.50 to £12 (self catering). Groups? lets talk business.

DIRECTIONS GR 566 638. 3½ miles from Llanberis on Bangor road B4547.

'TOTTERS'

Plas Porth Yr Aur
2 High Street
Caernarfon
Gwynedd
LL55 1RN

'Totters' is situated in the heart of the historic castle town of Caernarfon. Sheltered by the castles town wall, we are only 30 metres from the shores of the Menai Straits and get to see some fantastic sunsets. The town not only offers the visitor a huge selection of pubs and restaurants to choose from, but also acts as the perfect base for trips into the Snowdonia National Park. There is very good public transport in and out of the National Park.

The hostel is a 200 year old, five floored town house, which is fully heated with all the comforts of home. Continental breakfast and all bedding is provided in the overnight charge. We have a common room with TV and games, drying room, book exchange, dining room, bicycle hire and a secure left luggage facility. The bedrooms sleep either 4 or 6 and can be arranged as mixed or single sex dorms. There is also a separate family room. We're easy going and flexible. Check us out !!

TELEPHONE CONTACT Bob or Henry (01286) 672963
OPENING SEASON All year (opening easter 96)
OPENING HOURS All day access. Book in by 10pm.
NUMBER OF BEDS 24
BOOKING REQUIREMENTS Booking is essential for groups in June, July, August and September, 25% deposit required.
PRICE PER NIGHT £9 per person (includes breakfast and all bedding). Discounts for groups and long stays.

DIRECTIONS The hostel is beside the castle wall next to the Royal Welsh Yacht Club. Ask anybody.

OUTDOOR ALTERNATIVE
Cerrig-yr-Adar
Rhoscolyn, Holyhead
Anglesey, Gwynedd, LL65 2NQ

The centre is wonderfully situated in 7 acres of an 'Area of Outstanding Natural Beauty', 300m from the beach at the south end of Holy Island, Anglesey. Nearby Holyhead has intercity links and ferries to Ireland.

The centre is a splendid residential base for study, recreation or training in the outdoors. There is scope for natural history interests with spectacular geology and a range of habitats and species of birds and plants. There is evidence of occupation from pre-history and a varied and accessible coast provides good walking. For kayakers there are classic sea tours, overfalls, surf and rockhopping. Climbers have Gogarth nearby and Rhoscolyn offers all grades in an attractive setting. Divers can beach launch for local wrecks and scenic marine life. We can provide:- outdoor based development training, instruction in activities, guided walks, bird watching and local info. Camping with toilets and showers is also available and pub within walking distance.

TELEPHONE CONTACT Margaret,Ian or Chris (01407)860469
OPENING SEASON All year
OPENING HOURS 24 hr access
NUMBER OF BEDS 36
BOOKING REQUIREMENTS Essential for groups (deposit).
PRICE PER NIGHT £8.60 per person (inc VAT).

DIRECTIONS GR 278 752 From A5 traffic lights at Valley (Dyffryn) take B4545 (left) for Trearddur. In 1½m at Four Mile Bridge take left fork, signposted Rhoscolyn. After 1½m take a sharp left at the camping and caravanning symbols. In ½m fork right at large white gatepost. The centre is 300yds on the left.

The Isle of Anglesey
North Wales
Britain's Treasure Island

Anglesey can offer a kind of holiday that is increasingly rare. An unspoilt island with plenty of room to roam about - leave the crowds behind!

Discover an extraordinary variety of landscapes: rocky slabs and cliffs beneath luminous skies, small coves pounded by the waves, long stretches of sand and dune. There are broad estuaries bordered by woodlands and great expanses of rolling green pasture broken by outcrops of rock, small lakes and lonely marshes fringed by reeds. Wild life thrives in these habitats. Seabirds, rare elsewhere, nest on these cliffs in their thousands; geese, duck and wading birds seek out Anglesey's wetlands. Wild flowers abound, and include several rare species.

Make the most of your visit by sending for your FREE full colour comprehensive guide to the Island, available from the Tourist Information Centre, Holyhead Road, Llanfair PG, Anglesey, Gwynedd LL61 5UJ or telephone (O1248) 713177

SCOTLAND

	Pg	Phone
Glasgow Backpackers, 8 Park Circus, Glasgow, G3		(0141) 3325412
Strathclyde University Campus Village, Weaver Street, Glasgow, G1 0NG	68	(0141) 5534149
Princes Street Backpackers, 5 West Register Street, Edinburgh, EH2 2AA	69	(0131) 5566894
Kinnaird Christian Hostel, 14 Coates Crescent, Edinburgh, EH3 7AG	70	(0131) 225 3608
Royal Mile Backpackers, 105 High Street, Edinburgh, EH1 1SG	71	(0131) 5576120
High Street Hostel, 8 Blackfriars Street, Edinburgh, EH1 1NE	71	(0131) 5573984
North High Corrie Croft, Corrie, Isle of Arran, Scotland		(01770) 302203
Gannochy House, Uni. of St Andrews, North Street, St Andrews, Fife, KY16 9AJ	72	(01334) 464870
Braincroft Bunkhouse, Braincroft, Crieff, Perthshire, PH7 4JZ	73	(01764) 670140
Dunolly House, Taybridge Drive, Aberfeldy, Perthshire, PH15 2BL	74	(01887) 820298
Oban Backpackers, Breadalbane Street, Oban, Argyll, PA34 5NZ	71	(01631) 562107
Jeremy Inglis Hostel, 21 Airds Crescent, Oban Argyll, PA34 4BA	75	(01631) 565065
West Highland Lodge Bunkhouse, Kinlochleven, Argyll, PA40 4RQ	76	(01855) 831471
Leacantuim Farm Bunkhouse, Glencoe, Argyll, PA39 4HX	77	(01855) 811256
Inchree Bunkhouse, Onich, Fort William, PH33 6SD	78	(01855) 821287
Fort William Backpackers, Alma Road, Fort William, PH33 6HB	71	(01397) 700711

	Pg	Phone
Calluna, Heathercroft, Fort William, Inverness-shire, PH33 6RE	.	(01397) 700451
Smiddy Bunkhouse, Station Road, Corpach, Fort William, Inverness-shire, PH33 7LS	80	(01397) 772467
The Grey Corrie Lodge, Roy Bridge, Inverness-shire, PH31 4AN	81	(01397) 712236
Àite Cruinnichidh, 1 Achluachrach, By Roy Bridge, Invernesss-shire, PH31 4AW	82	(01397) 712315
Newtonmore Independent Hostel, Main Street, Newtonmore, PH20 1DA	83	(01540) 673360
Braemar Bunkhouse, Braemar Outdoor Centre, 15 Mar Road, Braemar, AB35 5YL	84	(013397) 41517
Glen Feshie Hostel, Balachroick House, Kincraig, Inveress-shire, PH21 1NH	85	(01540) 651323
Kirkbeag Hostel, Kirkbeag, Kincraig, Nr Kingussie, Inverness-shire, PH21 1ND	.	(01540) 651298
The Stop-Over, The Square, Grantown on Spey, Morayshire, PH26 3HQ	.	(01479) 872529
Fort Augustus Abbey Backpackers Lodge, Fort Augustus, Inverness-shire, PH32 4BD	86	(01320) 366703
Foyers House, Foyers, By Loch Ness, Inverness-shire, IV1 2XU	87	(01456) 486405
Loch Ness Backpackers, East Lewiston, Drumnadrochit, Inverness-shire, IV3 6UT	88	(01456) 450807
Glen Affric Backpackers Hostel, Cannich by Beauly, Inverness	89	(01456) 415263
Inverness Student Hotel, 8 Culduthel Road, Inverness, IV2 4AB	71	(01463) 236556
Skye Backpackers, Kyleakin, Isle of Skye, IV41 8PH	71	(01599) 534510
Fossil Bothy Independent Hostel, 13 Lower Breakish, Isle of Skye, IV42 8QA	90	(01471) 822297
Croft Bothy and Bunkhouse, Portnalong, Isle of Skye, IV47 8SL	91	(01478) 640254
Skyewalker Independent Hostel, Fiskavaig Road, Portnalong, Isle of Skye, IV47 8SL	92	(01478) 640250

	Pg	Phone
Portree Independent Hostel, The Green, Portree, Isle of Skye, IV51 9BT	93	(01478) 613737
Gerry's Achnashellach Hostel, Criag, Strathcarron, Wester-Ross, IV54 8YU	94	(01520) 766232
Badachro Bunkhouse, Hillcrest, Badachro, Gairloch, Ross-shire, IV21 2AA	95	(01445) 741291
Galson Farm Bunkhouse, South Galson, Isle of Lewis, HS2 0SH	96	(01851) 850492
Sàil Mhór Croft, Camusnagaul, Dundonnell, Ross-shire, IV23 2QT	97	(01854) 633224
Assynt Field Centre, Inchnadamph, Assynt, By Lairg, Sutherland, IV27 4HL	98	(01571) 822218
Kylesku Lodges, Kylesku, Near Unapool, Sutherland, IV27 4HW	99	(01971) 502003
The Focstle, The Strathy Inn, Strathy by Thurso, Caithness, KW14 7RY	100	(01641) 541205
Thurso Youth Club Hostel, Old Mill, Thurso, Caithness, KW14 8PS	101	(01847) 892964
Browns Hostel, Victoria Street, Stromness, Orkney KW16 3BS	102	(01856) 850661
Eviedale Bothy and Campsite, Evie, Orkney, KW17 2PJ	104	(01856) 751270
Betty Mouat's, Scatness, Virkie, Shetland. http://www.zetnet.co.uk/sigs/bods/	105	(01595) 693434
Böd of Nesbister, Whiteness, Shetland. http://www.zetnet.co.uk/sigs/bods/	105	(01595) 693434
The Sail Loft, Voe, Shetland http://www.zetnet.co.uk/sigs/bods/	105	(01595) 693434
Grieve House, Sodom, Whalsay, Shetland http://www.zetnet.co.uk/sigs/bods/	105	(01595) 693434
Johnnie Notion's Hamnavoe, Eshancss, Shetland http://www.zetnet.co.uk/sigs/bods/	105	(01595) 693434
Windhouse Lodge, Mid Yell, Shetland http://www.zetnet.co.uk/sigs/bods/	105	(01595) 693434

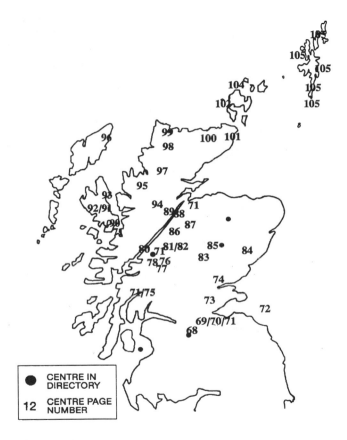

105
105
105
105
105

104
101
7

99
96
98
100
101

97
95
94 89 88 71
93 86 87
92/91 85 84
90 71 81/82 83
80 71 74
78 76
77 73 72
71/75 69/70/71
68

● CENTRE IN DIRECTORY

12 CENTRE PAGE NUMBER

STRATHCLYDE UNIVERSITY CAMPUS VILLAGE

Weaver Street
Glasgow
Glasgow, G1 0NG

Strathclyde University Campus Village is located in the centre of Glasgow, five minutes walk from Buchanan Street Bus Station and Queens Street Station. The accommodation is in modern flats on an attractively landscaped site. All rooms are singles with access to a comfortable lounge/kitchen area and adjacent to laundry facilities. They are built round the Lord Todd restaurant/bar which also houses a shop. Rooms are available with and without linen and self catering flats for small groups may be booked for three nights or more. Breakfast and other meals can be arranged in advance.

Glasgow city centre's shops, bars, restaurants, museums and many attractions are within walking distance or are easily reached by underground or bus.

TELEPHONE CONTACT Nicola Smith (0141) 553 4149
OPENING SEASON June to September inclusive
OPENING HOURS 24 hours
NUMBER OF BEDS 200 +
BOOKING REQUIREMENTS Phone in advance, groups should always book.
PRICE PER NIGHT From £9 per person (bed only)

DIRECTIONS From Queens Street Station proceed along Cathedral Street. Strathclyde University is on the right hand side and the student village is easy to find. The village office is in the Lord Todd Restaurant - turn right opposite the Clydesdale Bank, through the archway.

PRINCES STREET BACKPACKERS

5 West Register Street
Edinburgh
EH2 2AA

Your stay in this fascinating city will be carefree, with no curfew and no rules. Our central location has many benefits with the excitement of Princes Street at the foot of our stairs. Princes Street Backpackers has a laid back relaxed atmosphere and no school groups.

We have a pool room, laundry and ironing facilities, free lockup for valuables, self catering kitchen, lounge, dining room and TV room with video, Tourist Information, live entertainment guide and friendly helpful staff. Fresh bed linen is provided and included in the overnight charge and on Sunday we offer a free meal. Visa, Access and Mastercards accepted.

TELEPHONE CONTACT Jacque Kennedy (0131) 5566894
OPENING SEASON All year
OPENING HOURS 24 hours
NUMBER OF BEDS 120
BOOKING REQUIREMENTS One week in advance with a credit card number. No bookings are taken during the Edinburgh Festival or Christmas period.
PRICE PER NIGHT Dormitories £8.50 per person, 7th night free. After four weeks £7.00. Double room £22 per night.

DIRECTIONS We are situated directly between the central bus and train station. From Waverley Train Station, cross Princes Street and take road opposite (St Andrews Street) then take first right onto West Register Street, hostel on left.

KINNAIRD CHRISTIAN HOSTEL

14 Coates Crescent
Edinburgh
EH3 7AG

These fine Georgian houses provide accommodation for young women, married couples and families of any race or religion. Situated at the west end of Princes Street, convenient for bus and train stations, Kinnaird Christian Hostel has views of the castle and is near to public gardens.

The atmosphere is friendly and welcoming. There is no self catering but full breakfast and a supper-time drink is provided in the overnight fee. Accommodation is in single, twin and four bedded dormitories. Linen and towels provided for all and the single rooms have a tea tray. There is an elegant lounge with a TV and piano. There is also a quiet study room, laundry/drying room and public telephone (0131 226 2027). Let us welcome you to our city

TELEPHONE CONTACT (0131) 225 3608
OPENING SEASON All year, except Christmas week
OPENING HOURS 24 hour access, reception 9am to 10pm.
NUMBER OF BEDS 47
BOOKING REQUIREMENTS Booking is not essential, but one nights fee in deposit will secure you a bed.
PRICE PER NIGHT From £11 including linen, towels, breakfast and supper-time drink. Children 3-12 years half price, under 3 free.

DIRECTIONS From Waverley Train Station proceed to west end of Princes Street. Continue onto Shandwick place, take second turning on the right which is Coates Crescent.

71

GANNOCHY HOUSE
University of St Andrews
North Street
St Andrews
Fife
KY16 9AJ

Enjoy the attraction of beautiful St Andrews, 50 miles north of Edinburgh. Home of Scotland's oldest University, St Andrews still retains its medieval street plan and ancient architecture. The ruins of Scotland's largest cathedral and the Archbishop's castle blend with the old stone houses. There are beautiful coastal walks and as you would expect in the "Home of Golf", 5 ½ golf courses !

Our commitment is to provide clean, comfortable and warm accommodation at a budget price. Each room has a single bed and a wash-hand basin and is pleasantly furnished. Clean bed linen is provided but please bring your own towel. There are no catering facilities at Gannochy House but the cafes, restaurants and bars nearby offer a wide choice of meals. You can check in from 2.00pm to 6.00pm when our office is open. At other times please call the number below for availability. Check out time is 10.00am. We will require payment when you check in, either by cash or a cheque with a cheque guarantee card.

TELEPHONE CONTACT Linda Richardson (01334) 464870
OPENING SEASON June to September inclusive
OPENING HOURS All day access, office open 2pm to 6pm
NUMBER OF BEDS 80
BOOKING REQUIREMENTS Telephone before arrival
PRICE PER NIGHT £10 per person

DIRECTIONS Gannochy House is at the east end of North Street, next to Younger Hall.

BRAINCROFT BUNKHOUSE
Braincroft
Crieff
Perthshire
PH7 4JZ

Braincroft Bunkhouse is a recent high standard conversion of a 19th century farmstead. Accommodation is provided in two, four, six and eight bedded rooms (some are family rooms), many with private en-suite facilities. The bunkhouse has a large well equipped kitchen with excellent cooking and eating facilities. It also has a lounge, laundry, drying room and shop. Breakfast is available on request and we can provide transport.

This area of Perthshire is extremely popular with visitors. Glenturret Distillery, Auchingarrich Wildlife Centre, Drummond Fish Farm and Trout Fishery and Drummond Castle are all within 15 minutes drive of Braincroft. There are numerous walks of varying degree, watersports at Loch Earn, golfing on 31 different courses and fishing on some of Scotland's finest rivers. Guests at the bunkhouse also have access to the surrounding land, our own mountain bike course (with bike hire) and private fishing.

TELEPHONE CONTACT Neill (01764) 670140
OPENING SEASON All year
OPENING HOURS All day - no curfew
NUMBER OF BEDS 56
BOOKING REQUIREMENTS Booking is not essential but is recommended during June, July and August.
PRICE PER NIGHT £7 to £8 per person, group rates available
please enquire.

DIRECTIONS The bunkhouse is situated just off the A85 between Crieff (5 miles) and Comrie (2 miles). When travelling west from Crieff the entrance to the bunkhouse is on your right.

DUNOLLY HOUSE
Taybridge Drive
Aberfeldy
Perthshire
PH15 2BL

Dunolly House comprises of two units, the first is a 40 bed Victorian house, the other is a smaller 15 bed cottage. All rooms are fully carpeted and centrally heated with modern pine beds and a double bed (linen and duvets provided). The complex can be taken together or as separated units, with catering or self catering. We are licensed, there are areas for meetings and there is short tennis, volley ball, barbecue and other games in the grounds.

We are happy to arrange activities at the house or nearby activity centre. Listed below is a selection of what we have to offer:- rafting, kayaking, water skiing, wind surfing, sailing, power boat trips, parascending, Honda pilot racing, archery, clay pigeon shooting, mountain bike hire, sauna, cruise boat trips, fishing, orienteering, walks, treasure hunts, team games, overnight camp, putting, pony trekking, swimming and kite building.

TELEPHONE CONTACT Scot Hermiston (01887) 820298
OPENING SEASON All year
OPENING HOURS 24 hours
NUMBER OF BEDS 55
BOOKING REQUIREMENTS Not essential but recommended.
PRICE PER NIGHT £5.00 (low season), £8.25 (high season). discount for groups in low season.

DIRECTIONS Turn off the A9 Road at Ballinluig. Travel for 5 miles. Turn right at the T junction. Travel 6 miles until Aberfeldy. Continue through the main street and we are the last house on the right as you exit Aberfeldy.

JEREMY INGLIS HOSTEL

21 Airds Crescent
Oban
Argyll
PA34 4BA

Jeremey Inglis Hostel is only 150 yards from the station and the bus terminus in Oban. Prices include a continental breakfast with muesli, toast and home made jams, marmalade and Vegemite, etc. Tea and coffee are available at any time. The rooms are mostly double and family size so you have some privacy, all linen is included in the price. Kitchen facilities are provided and the hostel is heated by meter.

Please phone for bookings (01631) 565065 or 563064 if no reply.

TELEPHONE CONTACT Jeremy Inglis or Janette Forgrieve (01631) 65065/63064
OPENING SEASON All year
OPENING HOURS No curfew, access with key.
NUMBER OF BEDS 12 to 14
BOOKING REQUIREMENTS Booking preferred. Deposit in certain circumstances.
PRICE PER NIGHT £6.50 per person (inc breakfast)

DIRECTIONS **Office hours 9-5 Mon-Fri**, Find the tourist office, opposite is a small bakery (Lorn Backer), next door to McTavish's Kitchens Office. Please ask for Jeremy or Janette at McTavish's Office. **Non-Office hours** if McTavish's office is closed the hostel is round the nearest corner, 1st doorway, pink door, 2nd floor. If Jeremy is not in he's often to be found at Mctavish's Kitchens in George Street next to Woolworths and Boots (Tel (01631) 565065).

WEST HIGHLAND LODGE BUNKHOUSE

Kinlochleven
Argyll
PA40 4RQ

The West Highland Lodge is located in the village of Kinlochleven which lies in the heart of the Mamore Mountains. Ben Nevis lies to the north and Glencoe to the south. The area provides a unique diversity of walks, hikes, scrambles and climbs; summer and winter; from easy to extreme. The Lodge is ideal for walkers of the West Highland Way.

We offer comfortable accommodation comprising of seven rooms each sleeping 4 and one of 6. We have a fully equipped kitchen, dining room, showers and a drying room. There is also a payphone, television and pool table. Local amenities include a newsagent, Post Office, restaurant, pub, fish and chip shop, hardware store and supermarket. Guiding and instruction for hill walking and climbing, summer and winter, available on request.

TELEPHONE CONTACT Kevin/Tracey Beard (01855) 831471
OPENING SEASON All year
OPENING HOURS Flexible
NUMBER OF BEDS 34
BOOKING REQUIREMENTS Advisable
PRICE PER NIGHT £6 per person. Reduced rates for groups in the low season.

DIRECTIONS From the A82 Glasgow to Fort William road take the turn at Glencoe or at North Ballachulish signed to Kinlochleven. The hostel is 100 yards from the centre of Kinlochleven village. There is a regular bus service to the village from Glencoe, Ballachulish and Fort William.

LEACANTUIM FARM BUNKHOUSE
Glencoe
Argyll
PA39 4HX

Leacantuim Farm Bunkhouse is situated on a working farm in the magnificent valley of Glencoe, 16 miles from Fort William. The surrounding mountains are famous for ridge walks and climbs but also provide enjoyable fell walking for the prepared. Glencoe has a famous history of clan wars and a highland natural habitat. In a 15 mile radius you can try pony trekking, winter down hill skiing(with tow) or hire a boat. On the farm there are pools in the river suitable for swimming and fishing. Fishing permit needed.

The accommodation is provided in three units. The Bunkhouse sleeps 22 and has a drying room, the Alpine Barn sleeps 24 and is the cheapest accommodation and Ben End sleeps 12 and is only available to groups. All units are self contained with toilet/shower facilities and kitchen. If possible please bring sleeping bags and cooking/eating utensils. Bedding and dishes can be hired. Camping also available (20 acres).

TELEPHONE CONTACT Grant or MacColl (01855) 811256
OPENING SEASON All Year
OPENING HOURS Access between 10am to 4pm is available by arrangement.
NUMBER OF BEDS 64 in 3 units
BOOKING REQUIREMENTS Booking not required, but deposit will secure bed.
PRICE PER NIGHT £6.50 (Bunkhouse) or £5.50 (Alpine Barn). Ben End is available weekly to groups for £40 per person.

DIRECTIONS GR 116 577. On A82 Glencoe to Tyndrum Rd.

INCHREE BUNKHOUSE
Onich , Fort William
Highlands , PH33 6SD

Situated between Ben Nevis and Glencoe, in ideal walking country, with several walks straight from the site to waterfalls and to seal watch. We are centrally based for hill walking, climbing, canoeing, mountain biking, touring etc, and in winter for ice climbing, skiing and snow boarding. Check our three choice hire rates for mountain bikes, ski's and snowboards. We also provide maps and holiday/touring tips. Inchree bunkhouse provides comfortable, fully self catering accommodation with all facilities. There is one room with 2 doubles and 2 singles, one room with 7 singles, and the main room with an alpine sleeping platform for 12. Extra twin and double rooms are also available in chalets. The bunkhouse is heated by a woodburning stove, has full kitchen facilities, TV, hot showers, drying room, laundry and a climbing wall. Bedding provided at no extra charge when requested. Our on site pub/restaurant has real ales, real food and a log fire. There is a shop 600m away. Ideal small friendly centre for 1 to 25. Credit cards are accepted.

TELEPHONE/FAX CONTACT Paddy Heron (01855) 821287
OPENING SEASON All year
OPENING HOURS 24 hours
NUMBER OF BEDS 25 + 40 in 8 units.
BOOKING REQUIREMENTS Phone or turn up
PRICE PER NIGHT £5.70 to £8.50. Discount for 7 days.

DIRECTIONS From the south:- 4 miles north of Ballachulish bridge on A82, turn right (signed Inchree) up side road for 200 yds. From the north:- 8 miles from Fort William on A82, turn left (signed Inchree). On main bus route, ask for Inchree Junction 1/2 mile south of Corran Ferry. All buses stop here (local and long distance) ask for Inchree Road Junction.

THE SMIDDY BUNKHOUSE

The Old Smiddy
Station Road, Corpach
Fort William
Inverness-shire, PH33 7LS

The Smiddy Bunkhouse is an alpine style lodge overlooking the south west end of the Caledonian Canal. It provides top class bunkhouse accommodation with a pine clad interior and soft wall lighting to give a cosy atmosphere. The bunkhouse has a fully fitted kitchen (food available from local shop), drying room, two bunkrooms with alpine sleeping platforms (mattress, sleepingbag, liner and pillow supplied) and a comfortable sitting/dining area. The location of the bunkhouse is ideal for many outdoor activities and instruction and courses are available. Ben Nevis, The Mamores and Glen Coe provide all year round mountaineering opportunities. The area is also a canoe sport mecca with kayaking available on sea, river and loch. There are good rough terrain routes for mountain bikes and the hostel is on the Great Glen Cycle Route and two miles from the West Highland Way.

TELEPHONE CONTACT John or Tina (01397) 772467
OPENING SEASON All year
OPENING HOURS All day (with key). Key deposit required.
NUMBER OF BEDS 12
BOOKING REQUIREMENTS We cannot guarantee a bed unless a fee is paid. Credit card number taken as security.
PRICE PER NIGHT From £8 to £10 per person (inc bedding).

DIRECTIONS Take A82 north out of Fort William, towards Inverness, then A830 towards Mallaig and follow for 2½ miles to Corpach. Turn left immediately opposite Spar Shop, signposted 'Caledonian Canal'. The hostel is 30yds on the left. Two mins walk from Corpach Station, on the Fort William to Mallaig line.

THE GREY CORRIE LODGE

Roy Bridge
Inverness-shire
PH31 4AN

The Grey Corrie Lodge offers a base camp from which you can explore the Scottish Highlands. Whether you are an individual or part of an organised group you can exercise your adventurous spirit in the challenging Highland regions around Lochaber. The local attractions include Glen Roy for excellent scenery, Creag Meagaidh (3700ft) for a winter challenge, or the neighbouring Grey Corries (part of the Ben Nevis Range). Ben Nevis is a short distance to the south west and Glencoe offers worthy exploration.

The facilities are suitable for disabled persons and consist of bunkrooms for 2,4 or 8 persons. The lodge is complete with self catering facilities, heating, showers, toilets, drying rooms all bedding and a log fire. The lodge is adjacent to Roy Bridge Inn which can provide meals and there is music some Saturdays throughout the year

TELEPHONE CONTACT Nick or Sue Harding (01397) 712236
OPENING SEASON All year
OPENING HOURS All day
NUMBER OF BEDS 28
BOOKING REQUIREMENTS Can book with a deposit.
PRICE PER NIGHT £7.50 - £8.50 per person. (special rates for groups staying a week or more)

DIRECTIONS The lodge is in Roy Bridge. On the A82 to Spean Bridge, turn right to Roy Bridge. On A9 to Newtonmore turn left to Roy Bridge. Train station in Roy Bridge.

ÀITE CRUINNICHIDH

1 Achluachrach
By Roy Bridge
Near Fort William
Inverness-shire
PH31 4AW

Àite Cruinnichidh occupies a unique sheltered spot adjacent to the Monessie Gorge in an area long associated with Bonnie Prince Charlie and famous for remote glens, mountain passes and rare golden eagles. There are numerous easy walks within minutes of the hostel and 7 magnificent canoeing rivers within 20 miles. The location is also ideal for climbing, mountain biking and only 15 minutes drive from the ski slopes. Àite Cruinnichidh is a warm, comfortable, friendly country hostel in a converted barn, set in stunning surroundings near Roy Bridge. It is 15 miles north east of Fort William. We offer accommodation in six rooms (2 x 6 beds, 3 x 4 beds, 1 twin room) in comfortable pine bunk beds. We also offer mountain bike and backpacking tours into the remote areas of Scotland. We can advise you on local routes with maps available. So come and enjoy the hospitality of one of Scotland's best independent hostels.

TELEPHONE CONTACT (01397) 712315 Gavin or Nicola
OPENING SEASON All year
OPENING HOURS 24 hours
NUMBER OF BEDS 26
BOOKING REQUIREMENTS Booking advised, 50% deposit.
PRICE PER NIGHT £7 per person

DIRECTIONS From Fort William follow A82 for 10 miles to Spean Bridge, turn right onto A86 for 3 miles to Roy Bridge. Pass though village and continue for 2 miles. The hostel is 100 metres on the right after passing Glenspean Lodge Hotel on left.

NEWTONMORE INDEPENDENT HOSTEL

Craigellachie Lodge
Main Street, Newtonmore
Inverness-shire
PH20 1DA

Newtonmore, an attractive village in the Central Highlands, is the perfect base for outdoor activities, relaxing or touring. The village has shops, garage and several hotels which serve good value food and drink. The area has a colourful history, follow the Castle or Whisky trails, visit the Folk Park or the Steam Railway. You can walk, climb, ski, canoe, windsurf, cycle, fish, golf, birdwatch or sail, the choice is yours. Newtonmore Independent Hostel was purpose built in 1992. The hostel has lots of showers and toilets, brilliant drying room, well equipped kitchen and lounge/dining area with wood burning stove. **No Meters**. **Smoking is not allowed anywhere in the hostel**, smokers are welcome but must smoke outside. Inverness 46 miles, Fort William 50 miles, Glasgow/Edinburgh 110 miles. *Come and stay in our hostel, the area is unique, you will love it.*

TELEPHONE CONTACT Kathryn or Peter (01540) 673360
OPENING SEASON All year
OPENING HOURS All day, no curfew
NUMBER OF BEDS 18
BOOKING REQUIREMENTS Phone to check availability, especially for weekends and group bookings, 20% deposit.
PRICE PER NIGHT £8 per person, £56 - 8 beds, £112 - sole use.

DIRECTIONS GR 713 990. The hostel is in the centre of the village at the junction of the A86 and B9150, opposite the Craig Mhor Hotel, behind Craigellachie House. Railway station ½ mile, Buses from Inverness and Perth stop close to the hostel.

BRAEMAR BUNKHOUSE

Braemar Outdoor Centre
15 Mar Road
Braemar
AB35 5YL

Braemar Bunkhouse is an excellent base for walking, skiing and mountaineering trips in the Cairngorms and Grampians. Or just come and stay to explore the local area and savour the outstanding scenery.

Groups or individuals are equally welcome throughout the year. Sleeping a total of 26 the accommodation is split into rooms of 2,6,8 & 10 in three buildings, each with their own toilets and showers. For the bunkhouse (sleeping 10) sleeping bags are required. The other rooms have linen and duvets. All rooms are heated and the kitchens are fully equipped. Food can be bought locally. Drying facilities included with no meters! Mountain bikes are available for hire and we are happy to help with local information or walks. Nordic ski hire and courses are available in the winter (please phone for a brochure).

TELEPHONE/FAX CONTACT Malcolm (013397) 41517, fax 41496
OPENING SEASON All year
OPENING HOURS All hours (please enquire at Mountain Sports shop).
NUMBER OF BEDS 26
BOOKING REQUIREMENTS Booking is advised.
PRICE PER NIGHT £7 and £8 per person

DIRECTIONS GR 149 914 Braemar Bunkhouse is in the centre of the village, opposite the Fife Arms Hotel and to the right of The Mews. Bunkhouse sign is visible from main street. Buses from Aberdeen and Perth stop 200m from bunkhouse.

GLEN FESHIE HOSTEL

Balachroick House
Kincraig, Inverness-shire
PH21 1NH

Set in beautiful Glen Feshie with immediate access to the Cairngorm National Nature Reserve, this hostel is ideally placed for walking, climbing and cycling. In winter Glen Feshie is the perfect base to try cross-country ski touring. Both Nordic skiing equipment and mountain bikes can be hired from the hostel. Watersports and pony trekking are nearby for those with transport. The hostel has three bunkrooms each with four beds, a double room and a single room (duvets and linen provided). Hot showers, and good drying facilities are available. The kitchen is fully equipped for self catering and there is a wood buring stove in the common room/dining area. Porridge is provided free for breakfast and other meals including vegetarian/vegan meals can be provided with notice. There is a small store selling essentials, homemade bread, free range eggs and other goodies.

TELEPHONE CONTACT Jean Hamilton (01540) 651323
OPENING SEASON All year
OPENING HOURS All day - 24 hours
NUMBER OF BEDS 15
BOOKING REQUIREMENTS Booking advised at weekends.
PRICE PER NIGHT £7 per person (including porridge for breakfast), £24 for family bunkroom (4/5 beds), £70 whole hostel.

DIRECTIONS GR 849 009. From Kingussie take B9151 to Kincraig. Turn right at Kincraig, down unclassified road, after 2km turn left onto the B970 towards Feshibridge. After crossing the River Feshie in 1.5km, turn right onto a road signposted Achleanant hostel, follow for 2½miles.

FORT AUGUSTUS ABBEY
BACKPACKERS LODGE
Fort Augustus
Inverness-shire, PH32 4BD

A friendly welcome awaits you at this unusual hostel in the gate-lodge of the historic Fort Augustus Abbey. Accommodation is in small rooms (maximum of four beds) all with en-suite wash basins. Right in the centre of the village the lodge is very close to a good variety of shops, pubs and eating places, and meals may also be taken in the Abbey. There is a well equipped kitchen and plenty of hot water, with a choice of bath or shower.

Situated at the head af Loch Ness and beside the Caledonian Canal, the lodge is also convenient for the Corrieyairick Pass and the Great Glen Cycle Route, making it an ideal base for walking, cycling or touring holidays. Mountain bikes may be hired locally and the Abbey Heritage Centre is well worth a visit. Other activities include pony trekking, golf, cruises on Loch Ness and a visit to the Young Clansman's Black House. *Once here you'll want to stay longer.*

TELEPHONE CONTACT Fran Haggerty (01320) 366703 / 366233
OPENING SEASON April to October
OPENING HOURS Staff available 7am to 12 noon and 6pm to 11pm. Access available 11am to 11pm.
NUMBER OF BEDS 18
BOOKING REQUIREMENTS Booking advised, July and Aug.
PRICE PER NIGHT £8 per person.

DIRECTIONS GR 980 091. The hostel is the gate lodge of St Benedicts Abbey, situated at the junction of Inverness, Fort William and Whitebridge Roads. Walking from the Tourist Office, cross canal bridge and the Abbey is 250yds ahead.

FOYERS HOUSE
Foyers
By Loch Ness
Inverness-shire
IV1 2XU

Foyer house is a small, family run, hostel situated at Upper Foyers near the waterfall on the secluded south side of Loch Ness (B852). We offer warm, comfortable accommodation in twin or family rooms. We have a licensed bar, self catering kitchen and a comfortable lounge with TV and log fire. We also offer inexpensive good home cooking.

Foyers village is in the county of Stratherrick, an unspoilt area of wild and beautiful landscapes. Ancient picts, celtic clans and proud Jacobites all lived and died here leaving a rich tapestry of legend, hillforts and monuments to mark their passage. An excellent base for walking cycling fishing or doing absolutely nothing. Relax on our terraced roof with breathtaking views over the loch, who knows you may even get a glimpse of Nessie !

TELEPHONE CONTACT Neil or Brenda (01456) 486405
OPENING SEASON All year
OPENING HOURS All day
NUMBER OF BEDS 17
BOOKING REQUIREMENTS 24h advance booking advised in Aug, credit card to guarantees, otherwise beds sold after 6pm.
PRICE PER NIGHT £8 (£10 including linen)

DIRECTIONS GR 499205. From Inverness take B862 past the castle to Dores. Where road forks take B852 along loch to Foyers. From Fort Augustus take B862 to Whitebridge, turn left B852 to Foyers. From A9 Daviot take B851 signposted to Fort Augustus, one mile before Whitebridge, turn right, B852 to Foyers. Foyers House is next to Foyers Store/Post Office.

LOCH NESS BACKPACKERS

Coiltie Farmhouse
East Lewiston
Drumnadrochit
Inverness-shire, IV3 6UT

Loch Ness Backpackers Lodge is the perfect base from which to enjoy the mystic atmosphere and outstanding scenery which surrounds Loch Ness and Urquhart Castle. The beauty of the area makes it ideal for walking, cycling, horse riding, fishing, photography, or just cruising on the Loch. All of these activities are within walking distance of the Lodge, as are the Loch Ness Exhibition Centre, restaurants, bank, post office, bus, and pubs where you can have a drink and a friendly chat with the locals.

The Lodge is a cosy and friendly place to unwind in a very relaxed atmosphere. We have two lounges with coal/log fires (one with TV and Video), two fully equipped self catering kitchens, an excellent BBQ area, hot showers and very comfy beds already made up with sheets and duvets (included in price).
A home from home.

TELEPHONE CONTACT (01456) 450807
OPENING SEASON All year
OPENING HOURS All day, no curfew.
NUMBER OF BEDS 32
BOOKING REQUIREMENTS Booking advised in peak season
PRICE PER NIGHT From £8 / £8.50 per person. Enquire for group discounts.

DIRECTIONS Hostel is near the A82 Inverness to Fort William road. From Inverness, go through Drumnadrochit to Lewiston. Hostel signed first left after Smiddy Pub. From Fort William, hostel turn off is right after the stone bridge in Lewiston.

GLEN AFFRIC
BACKPACKERS HOSTEL
Cannich By Beauly
Inverness

Glen Affric Backpackers Hostel, formerly a forestry hostel, has been totally refurbished to a high standard. The bedrooms accommodate one or two people in bunkbeds and are heated by coin operated radiators. Family rooms are also available. There is a comfortable common room with log fire and TV. We also have self catering and laundry facilities.

The hostel is situated in the village of Cannich in the heart of the highlands, surrounded by spectacular scenery. There is an abundance of famous Munroes in the area. Local facilities include, a hotel, shop, restaurant and plenty of first class trout and salmon fishing. We can arrange transport, boat trips, hill walking, pony trekking, trips to see wild deer, local distillery visits, clay pigeon shoots, shopping trips and we have mountain bikes for hire. We can also offer camping facilities and caravan pitches on land adjacent to the hostel.

TELEPHONE CONTACT Kath Gregory (01456) 415263 / 415364
OPENING SEASON 1st January to 30th November
OPENING HOURS 24 hours
NUMBER OF BEDS 40
BOOKING REQUIREMENTS Individuals are advised to phone ahead. Groups should book with 10% deposit.
PRICE PER NIGHT £4.80 per person.

DIRECTIONS Take A82 out of Inverness to Drumnadrochit, then take signs for Cannich (A831). Upon entering Cannich look for hostel sign on left. There is a bus to Cannich from Inverness.

FOSSIL BOTHY INDEPENDENT HOSTEL

13 Lower Breakish
Isle of Skye
IV42 8QA

Situated right on the seashore, Fossil Bothy has spectacular views of the mountains and sea. Watch seals swimming by only yards away, or stately herons fishing in the estuary silhouetted against cosmic sunsets. Find the giant fossils along the shore, and in the walls of the building. A tranquil, relaxing haven for weary travellers, the bothy is the perfect base to explore the beautiful Isle of Skye, for country walks or energetic climbs, for divers and nature-lovers. Visit the distillery, go fishing, admire the scenery, learn our history and geology. The Bothy is unique; an imaginatively restored steading with many unusual decorative features - ideal for groups or individuals. Shops and pubs within 3 miles, the excellent Seagull Restaurant a few minutes walk. Bike hire nearby. Transport to/from the ferry is usually possible. Come with friends, or make new ones while you're here. Please phone for a leaflet, or to book.

TELEPHONE CONTACT Fiona (01471) 822297 (evenings and weekends) (01471) 822644 (weekdays)
OPENING SEASON Before Easter to end of October
OPENING HOURS All day
NUMBER OF BEDS 8
BOOKING REQUIREMENTS Prior telephone booking is essential
PRICE PER NIGHT £6.50 per person. Discounts for groups of 8 booking for one week or more.

DIRECTIONS The hostel is five miles north of new Kyle bridge. Full directions will be given when you phone to book.

CROFT BOTHY AND BUNKHOUSE

Portnalong
Isle of Skye
IV47 8SL

The Croft Bunkhouse and Bothy are two comfortable fully equipped hostels situated on the west coast of Skye on a 12 acre croft that has views over the sea and mountains. Owned by a retired mountain guide they provide inexpensive, self catering accommodation for individuals or groups. The local pub 500yds away arranges sea fishing trips and there is a shop 600yds. There are enjoyable coastal and moorland walks from the bunkhouse and the Cuillins are only 20 minutes drive away at Glenbrittle or Sligachan. Mountain bikes are available for hire (£5 a day to residents) and map loan is free. The Bunkhouse also has a games room with table tennis and dart board, sleeps 14. The Bothy sleeps 6 and is an ideal family unit or a cosy winter retreat.

TELEPHONE/FAX CONTACT Pete Thomas (01478) 640254
OPENING SEASON All year
OPENING HOURS No curfew
NUMBER OF BEDS Bunkhouse 14, Bothy 6
BOOKING REQUIREMENTS Phone bookings held to 6pm. Advance payment guarantees bed (Visa/Access accepted).
PRICE PER NIGHT £5.50 per person, no hidden extra charges. Group bookings up to 10% discount. Camping £2.50 to £4.50.

DIRECTIONS GR 348 353. When driving, from Sligachan take the A863 for 4 miles then left onto B8009, follow this road through the village of Carbost to Portnalong, the Bunkhouse is signposted and opposite the Little Gallery. There is a regular bus service (weekdays only) from Portree and Sligachan to Portnalong (01478 640400). Collection by hostel minibus by arrangement at weekends and evenings.

SKYEWALKER INDEPENDENT HOSTEL

Old School, Fiskavaig Road
Portnalong, Isle of Skye
IV47 8SL

Situated close to the Cuillin hills on the beautiful Minginish Peninsula the old village school has been tastefully converted to very high standards of comfort and has all the normal features and more! The hostel is centrally heated throughout and provides plenty of hot water and more than adequate shower and toilet facilities. The village Post Office and a small shop are housed within the hostel and for those not wishing to use the well fitted kitchen at any time a good cafe is situated in the hostel grounds. The pub is 5 minutes walk away, and beaches and beautiful walks are nearby. All entrances are ramped to provide full wheelchair access throughout the hostel. Bed linen included and no meters! The perfect base for outdoor activities with hill, moors and water all combining into spectacular scenery - and a hot shower and comfortable bed to finish the day.

TELEPHONE CONTACT Trevor or June (01478) 640250
OPENING SEASON All year
OPENING HOURS 24 hour access
NUMBER OF BEDS 30
BOOKING REQUIREMENTS In peak season booking 4 weeks in advance is advised (deposit required)
PRICE PER NIGHT £6 per person (reduced rates in winter)

DIRECTIONS GR 348 348. From Sligachan take A863 then B8009 through Carbost and Fermilea to Portnalong. At the bus stop turn left onto Fiskavaig Road, walk 500m to hostel. Two local buses run each weekday.

PORTREE INDEPENDENT HOSTEL

The Green
Portree
Isle of Skye, IV51 9BT

Centrally situated in Portree, the capitol of Skye, this hostel provides quality inexpensive self catering accommodation with a communal fully equipped kitchen (continental breakfast is available on request). Originally the islands main post office it has been converted to an independent hostel sleeping 50 in dormitories of 6-8, all bedding provided, there is also a launderette on site. Only 100 metres from the bus terminus it is an ideal base for touring the Island or as a starting off point to other hostels in the North and West of Skye which are served by public transport. Within easy walking distance there are a wide variety of shops, pubs and eating out facilities that vary from chip shop, chinese carry-outs and bar snacks to "Taste of Scotland" restaurants. From the hostel there are pleasant coastal and woodland walks and bike hire is available locally. Portree holds an annual Folk Festival in July and the Highland games in Aug.

TELEPHONE/FAX CONTACT The manager (01478) 613737
OPENING SEASON All year **(opening May 96)**
OPENING HOURS No curfew
NUMBER OF BEDS 50
BOOKING REQUIREMENTS Phone bookings held to 6pm. Advance payment guarantees bed. Visa/Access accepted.
PRICE PER NIGHT £7.50 to £8.50 per person.

DIRECTIONS Situated 50 metres from the main square in the town. Approaching Portree on the A850 road from the mainland the hostel is between the long stay car park and the town centre.

GERRYS ACHNASHELLACH HOSTEL

Criag, Achnashellach
Strathcarron, Wester-Ross
Scotland, IV54 8YU

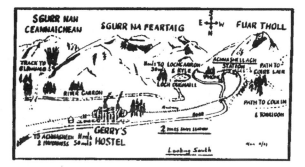

Gerry's Hostel is situated in an excellent mountaineering and wilderness area on the most scenic railway in Britain. The hostel has a common room with log fire, library and stereo. Come and go as you please. Camping available. No TV. No smoking.

TELEPHONE CONTACT Gerry (01520) 766232
OPENING SEASON All Year
OPENING HOURS Never closed
NUMBER OF BEDS 30
BOOKING REQUIREMENTS Prepay booking to secure bed, or phone or just arrive.
PRICE PER NIGHT From £7.00 per person. 10% discount for large groups or long stays.

DIRECTIONS GR 037 493. On the A890 from Fort William to Inverness. Hostel situated 2 miles east of Achnashellach Station.

BADACHRO BUNKHOUSE
Badachro Village
Gairloch
Ross-shire
IV21 2AA

Situated only 100 yards from the sea this comfortable bunk house offers accommodation for individuals, families or groups. We can arrange a variety of activities which include sailing (dinghys or yachts), canoeing, sea angling, small boat hire, hill-walking, freshwater fishing, golfing, beach barbecues and visits to Inverewe Gardens or Gairloch Museum. These activities can be arranged for individuals or groups. The local pub is only a few minutes walk and there is a sea taxi service to Gairloch from the jetty by the pub. The accommodation is in three areas, one of which can be booked as a private room (sleeping up to five). There are two kitchens and there is ample hot water.

Brochure on accommodation and activities on request.

TELEPHONE/FAX CONTACT Ian Thomson (01445) 741291 / 712458, fax (01445) 712511
OPENING SEASON All year
OPENING HOURS 24hr access. Please arrive between 9am and 12 midnight.
NUMBER OF BEDS 13
BOOKING REQUIREMENTS Booking strongly recommended
PRICE PER NIGHT £7 per person, duvet or sleeping bag £2 extra. Groups discounts available.

DIRECTIONS GR 778 737. The bunkhouse is signposted in Badachro village (on the B8056) and at the main road junction at Kerry Bridge (2 miles away) on the Gairloch/Achnasheen Road (A832). Westerbus from Inverness to Gairloch and train from Inverness to Achnasheen - we can arrange a lift - please discuss.

GALSON FARM BUNKHOUSE
Galson Farm House
South Galson
Isle of Lewis
HS2 0SH

Galson Farm Bunkhouse is situated on a croft on the west coast of Lewis overlooking the Atlantic Ocean, and is ideal for exploring the Islands sandy beaches, mountains and burns, either on foot or by bicycle (cycle hire in Stornoway). The shore lies just a short walk through the croft and is ideal for fishing, bird-watching, walking, sailing and beach combing. The farm is part of a crofting village where Gaelic is the everyday language. We are twenty miles from Stornoway and eight miles from Butt of Lewis Lighthouse. The bus stops at Galson village road end.

Our newly opened bunkhouse has one dormitory with eight bunks and two shower rooms. Bedding can be supplied if required or bring your own. There is a full kitchen/dining room so that you can self-cater or you can order meals. Come and go as you please. Shop and pub two miles away, advance booking advisable and essential for groups, Access/Visa facility.

TELEPHONE/FAX CONTACT Dorothy and John Russell (01851) 850492
OPENING SEASON All year
OPENING HOURS All day - 24 hours
NUMBER OF BEDS 8
BOOKING REQUIREMENTS Always phone in advance. Bookings held till 6pm, deposit (visa/access) guarantees bed.
PRICE PER NIGHT £7 per person

DIRECTIONS GR 437 592. Follow A857 Stornoway to Ness(Nis) road for 20 miles. At Galson (Gabhsann) turn left at the telephone kiosk. Bunkhouse is ¼ mile further on.

SÀIL MHÓR CROFT
Camusnagaul
Dundonnell
Ross-shire, IV23 2QT

Sàil Mhór Croft is a small luxury hostel which is situated at Dundonnell on the shores of Little Loch Broom. The mountain range of An Teàllach, which has the reputation of being one of the finest ridge walks in great Britain, is right on our doorstep and the area is a haven for walkers of all experiences as well as for photographers. Whether you wish to climb the summits, walk along the loch side, have an afternoon up Sàil Mhór or just soak up the tranquillity of the area, you know the scenery cannot be beaten anywhere in the country.

The hostel offers accommodation for up to 16 persons in three dorms. You have the choice of using our self catering facilities or we can provide a full breakfast and evening meal if required. It is advisable to ring in advance in order to book yourself a bed.

TELEPHONE CONTACT Dave or Lynda (01854) 633224
OPENING SEASON All year, except Xmas and New Year
OPENING HOURS Flexible
NUMBER OF BEDS 16
BOOKING REQUIREMENTS Always phone in advance. Groups should book as soon as possible.
PRICE PER NIGHT £7.00 to £7.50 per person

DIRECTIONS GR 064 893 (sheet 19) 1½ miles west of Dundonnell Hotel on A832. Daily mail bus runs Achnasheen-Gairloch-Dundonnell-Braemore Junction and back to Dundonnell. Wester Bus run to and from Inverness on Mon, Wed and Sat.

ASSYNT FIELD CENTRE

Inchnadamph Lodge
Inchnadamph, Assynt
By Lairg, Sutherland
IV27 4HL

Assynt is officially designated a National Scenic Area. The dramatic mountains (Suilven, Quinag, Canisp, Stac Pollaidh and Cul Mor) rise up as isolated peaks from rocky moorland inundated with lochans. Two national nature reserves are host to a wide diversity of birds, animals and plants (including rare species on the limestone at Inchnadamph). Interesting rock formations provide excitement for geologists and nearby lochs are popular for trout and salmon fly fishing - permits required. A mixture of twin, family and bunk rooms are available in the Lodge, which sits below Ben More Assynt, with views across Loch Assynt. Wood burning stoves are provided in the lounge and dining room. There is a fully equipped self-catering kitchen, continental breakfast is provided inclusive in the overnight fee and packed lunches are available on request. Bar meals are available in the adjacent Inchnadamph Hotel. Email contact available on assynt@presence.co.uk and full details and photos on the internet at http://www.presence.co.uk/assynt/

TELEPHONE CONTACT Chris (01571) 822218
OPENING SEASON All year (opens May 1996)
OPENING HOURS 24 hours
NUMBER OF BEDS 50
BOOKING REQUIREMENTS Booking advised
PRICE PER NIGHT £8.50 to £9.25 (dormitory), £10.50 to £11.25 (twin room). Including continental breakfast and linen. Discounts of up to 10% available for groups.

DIRECTIONS Inchnadamph is 25 miles north of Ullapool on the Lochinver/Durness road. The lodge is the big white building.

KYLESU LODGES
Kylesku
Near Unapool
Sutherland
IV27 4HW

Kylesku is ideally situated for exploring the rugged beauty of North West Sutherland, one of Britians' last remaining areas of true wilderness. Our independently run, self catering lodges overlook Loch A'Chairn Bhain with extensive views of the surrounding mountains. It is here that you may glimpse the rare Golden Eagle soaring above Quinag Mountain or watch the shy otters along our secluded shore.

The two lodges provide excellent facilities for individuals, couples or small groups, for one or more nights. Each lodge sleeps six in comfortable twin bedded rooms. The price of £8 per person per night includes all bedding, hot bath or shower and shared use of fully equipped kitchen. **The Lodges are strictly non-smoking**. Kylesku village is nearby with small hotel, bar, post office and harbour where boat trips can be taken to see Britians' highest waterfall. Local activities include walking, climbing, fishing and bird watching.

TELEPHONE CONTACT André (01971) 502003
OPENING SEASON March to October inclusive.
OPENING HOURS Please arrive before 9pm and be prepared to leave by 9am. Daytime access is available by arrangement.
NUMBER OF BEDS 12
BOOKING REQUIREMENTS Groups should book.
PRICE PER NIGHT From £8 to £10 per person.

DIRECTIONS The lodges are situated on the West Sutherland Coastal Route, 35 miles north of Ullapool on the A894. The nearest shop, at Scourie, is 9 miles away so bring your own food.

THE FOCSTLE
The Strathy Inn
Strathy by Thurso
Caithness
KW14 7RY

Welcome to the Focstle and to the Flow Country. The Focstle offers a good standard of budget accommodation in two dormitories of six and eight beds. We are next door to the Strathy Inn which offers good food and a convivial atmosphere.

There is an excellent surfing beach adjacent to the hostel, a rugged coastline to explore and unspoiled countryside walks to enjoy. The nature reserve at Strathy Point is good for migrating birds in May and September, some rare flowing plants in June and July and unusual insect eating plants. It is also a good vantage point to observe various species of whales, dolphins and basking sharks from the end of August. The sea fishing is good too. Inland the countryside hosts spectacular views and an abundance of wildlife with some good Brown Trout fishing on the remote lochs.

Come - Its worth it !

TELEPHONE/FAX CONTACT (01641) 541205, Fax 541385
OPENING SEASON Easter to November (inclusive)
OPENING HOURS Staffed 9am to 9pm. 24 hour access.
NUMBER OF BEDS 14
BOOKING REQUIREMENTS Parties of up to six or eight people, wishing to reserve a dormitory for sole use should book and confirm with deposit.
PRICE PER NIGHT £8.50 per person

DIRECTIONS GR 830 650. On the north coast of Scotland. On the A836 Thurso (21 miles) to Tongue (20 miles) Road.

THURSO YOUTH CLUB HOSTEL
Old Mill
Millbank
Thurso
KW14 8PS

Thurso Youth Club Hostel is an ideal stop on the way to the Orkney Ferry. Thurso is a friendly place with many shops and a couple of tourist attractions within the town. It has a beautiful beach and some fine river walks. You can walk from the hostel, though the town, along the cliffs to Holborn Head and see the fascinating blow holes. Alterrnativily, hire a bike and travel east to Dunnet Head, the most northly point on the mainland. Mingle with the locals in one of the many friendly informal bars and sample a range of malt whiskies. Finish off with a Haggis supper from Robin's Chip Shop or a pizza from Sandra's.

If requested meals can be provided at the hostel at a small cost.

TELEPHONE CONTACT Neil Watson (01847) 892964
OPENING SEASON July and August
OPENING HOURS 24 hours
NUMBER OF BEDS 22
BOOKING REQUIREMENTS Booking is helpful
PRICE PER NIGHT £8

DIRECTIONS From Tourist Information Centre:- follow the river past road traffic bridge to the foot bridge - cross the river. From Railway station:- turn right down Lovers Lane, at the bottom turn left, walk 25m, turn right, cross the foot bridge. Ask for the swimming pool, we are behind the church nearby.

BROWNS HOSTEL
Victoria Street
Stromness
Orkney
KW16 3BS

This family run hostel is ideally situated in the centre of a small fishing town, **Stromness**. It makes an excellent base for the tourist - a few minutes walk from the ferry terminal and bus stops. There is a bus service to Kirkwall every few hours Monday to Saturday. Bus tours also run every day and cycles are available for hire to visit the various sites of interest - **Skara Brae, Maeshowe, Standing Stones** etc. Ferries run to the smaller islands daily. In summer there is daylight all evening and one can stroll through our peaceful town and along the shore to watch the seals. Our kitchen/common room looks onto the street and coming back from a pleasant walk to chat to the other hostellers over a warm cup of tea seems to be a popular way of relaxing before going to bed. There are 2,3 or 4 beds per dorm and there is **no curfew**. There is a provisions shop nearby and the bakehouse across the street is open at 7.30am selling new bread and rolls for your breakfast.

TELEPHONE CONTACT Mrs Brown (01856) 850661
OPENING SEASON All year
OPENING HOURS All day
NUMBER OF BEDS 20
BOOKING REQUIREMENTS Booking advisable during March to October. Only prepaid bookings are taken.
PRICE PER NIGHT £7.00 - £7.50 per person.

DIRECTIONS By train or bus to Thurso, bus 1 mile to Scrabster then boat to Stromness. Five minutes walk from boat to hostel. Alternative route from John O'Groats by boat to Burwick then bus to Kirkwall Stromness.

ORKNEY ISLANDS

Summer passenger Ferry from
JOHN O'GROATS

MV Pentland Venture Every Day 26 Aprill to 30 September 1996.

	All Season	June, July, Aug	Until 10 Sept	From 11 Sept
Dep John O'Groats	9.00am	10.30am 4.15pm	6.00pm	4.30pm
Dep Burwick	9.45am	11.30am 5.15pm	7.00pm	5.30pm

Special off peak return to Kirkwall.

£20

Depart John O'Groats any afternoon.
Return from Orkney any morning.
(Free bus for ferry meets afternoon train
approx 2.30pm at Thurso Rail Station every day).

OR, Travel to & from Orkney direct from
INVERNESS

on

The Orkney Bus

Special return fare £35

(leaves Inverness Bus Station every day)

NORTHBOUND	SOUTHBOUND
Dep Inverness 2.20pm	Dept Kirkwall 9.00am
Arr Kirkwall 7.30pm	Arr Inverness 1.45pm

JOHN O'GROATS FERRIES, Ferry Office
John O'Groats, Caithness, KW1 4YR.
Tel (01955) 611353 FAX (01955) 611301

EVIEDALE BOTHY

Evie, Orkney
KW17 2PJ

Eviedale Bothy is a small renovated one room cottage. A lean-to annex contains free gas cooking with utensils provided, hot and cold water and a flush toilet. Showers may be taken across the road at the camp site. The common room contains four bunks, dining table, easy chairs and a solid fuel stove. Bedding is not provided so please bring your sleeping bag. Electricity is by coin meter. Across from the bothy the "Dale Kitchen" restaurant provides coffee and tea by the mug and lunches and teas of good wholesome home made fare. There is also a provisions shop and pub 200yds from the hostel.

The bothy is 10 minutes walk from Aikerness Sands and 1¾miles from the Broch of Gurness. We have available for guests a selection of mountain bikes. Fly fishing tackle can be hired, loch boats arranged and instruction for beginners provided. Camping is also available.

TELEPHONE CONTACT Mr Heaton (01856) 751 270 or Mr and Mrs Richardson (01856) 751 254
OPENING SEASON 1st April to 31st October
OPENING HOURS Flexible
NUMBER OF BEDS 4
BOOKING REQUIREMENTS Booking with full payment advisable in summer.
PRICE PER NIGHT £4 per person. Sole use £15 p/n, £75 p/w.

DIRECTIONS Take the A966 in Finstown (on the Kirkwall to Stromness road) for 8 miles. Hostel is in Evie village opposite Dale Kitchen restaurant. Enquiries at restaurant or Dale Farm.

Shetland Camping Böds

In Shetland, a Böd was a building used to house fishermen and their gear during the fishing season. Today we've borrowed the word to describe basic accomodation for those who want a simple holiday in our islands.

Böds are very basic, some Böds in remote locations have no electricity or lighting. However, each Böd has a space for cooking , eating & sleeping. There is a cold water supply and toilet facilities. A table, benches, a broom, dustpan and washing up bowl are provided.Both sexes share the same sleeping area and you must be prepared to share with other visitors, but that's part of the fun of a Böd holiday !

Call us for a Leaflet & Booking Form

Shetland Islands Tourism
Market Cross, Lerwick, Shetland, ZE1 0LU
Tel: (01595) 693434   Fax: (01595)695807

IRELAND

Causeway Coast Hostel, 4 Victoria Terrace, Portstewart, Co Derry, UK	109	(01265) 833789
Gortin Outdoor Centre, Glenpark Road, Gortin, Omagh, Co Tyrone, UK	110	(01662) 648770
Omagh Independent Hostel, 9a Waterworks Road, Omagh, Co Tyrone, UK	111	(01662) 241973
Bunnaton Hostel, Bunnaton, Glenvar, Letterkenny, Co Donegal	112	(074) 50122
Finn Farm (Pony Trekking) Hostel, Cappry, Ballybofrey, Co Donegal	113	(074) 32261
Greene's Holiday Hostel, Carnmore Road, Dungloe, Co Donegal	114	(075) 21021
Campbell's Holiday Hostel, Main Street, Glenties, Co Donegal	115	(075) 51491
Dún Ulín House, Kilcar, Co Donegal	116	(073) 38137
Sandville House, Ballyconnell, Co Cavan	117	(049) 26297
Town Clock Hostel, Town Centre, Carrick-on-Shannon, Co Leitrim	118	(078) 20068
Kilcommon Lodge Hostel, Pullathomas / Ballina, Co Mayo	119	(097) 84621
Club Atlantic, Altamount Street, Westport, Co Mayo	120	(098) 26644
Delphi Hostel, Delphi, Leenane, Co Galway	·	(095) 42246
The Old Monastery, Letterfrack, Connemara, Co Galway	121	(095) 41132
Inishbofin Island Hostel, Inishbofin, Co Galway	122	(095) 45855
Galway City Hostel, 25-27 Dominick Street Lower, Galway, Co Galway	123	(091) 566267
Mainistir House Hostel, Inismôr, Co Galway	124	(099) 61169
Kincora House and the Burren Holiday Hostel, Lisdoonvarna, Co Clare	125	(065) 74300
The Cottage, Lissylisheen, Kilcorney Road, Kilfenora, Co Clare	·	No Phone
Boghill Centre, Boghill, Kilfenora, Co Clare	126	(065) 74644

	Name	No.	Phone
	Clyde House, St Alponsus Street, Limerick	127	(061) 314357
	Lynchs Hostel, Castlegregory Village, Co Kerry	128	(066) 39128
	Bog View Hostel, Lougher, Inch, Annascaul, Co Kerry	129	(066) 58125
	The Ring Lyne, Chapeltown, Valentia Island, Co Kerry	130	(066) 76103
	Climbers Inn, Glencar, Co Kerry	131	(066) 60101
	Fossa Holiday Hostel, Fossa, Killarney, Co Kerry	132	(064) 31497
	Atlas House Budget Accommodation, Park Road, Killarney, Co Kerry	133	(064) 36144
	Carrigbeg Independent Holiday Hostel, Caherdaniel, Killarney, Co Kerry	.	(066) 75229
	Garranes Farmhouse Hostel, Cahermore, Beara, Co Cork	134	(027) 73147
	Tig Barra, Ballingeary, Co Cork	.	(026) 47016
	Shiplake Mountain Hostel, Dunmanway, Co Cork	135	(023) 45750
	Harbour View Small Independent Hostel, Harbour View, Bantry, Co Cork	136	(027) 51140
	Rolf's Holiday Hostel, Baltimore, West Co Cork	.	(028) 20289
	Cork City Independent Hostel, 100 Lower Glanmire Road, Cork City	137	(021) 509089
	Cashel Holiday Hostel, 6 John Street, Cashel, Co Tipperary	138	(062) 62330
	Cranagh Castle, Templetuohy, Templemore, Cc Tipperary	139	(0504) 53104
	Ormonde Accommodation Centre, John's Greer, Kilkenny, Co Kilkenny	140	(056) 52733
	Bunclody Holiday Hostel, Old School House, Ryland Road, Bunclody, Co Wexford	.	(054) 76076
	Creidum Hostel, Kishavanna, Edenderry, Co Offaly	.	(0405) 32166
	Student Care Accommodation, 114 Lower Baggct Street, Dublin 2	141	(01) 6616516
	Morehampton House Tourist Hostel, 78 Morehampton Road, Donnybrook, Dublin 4	142	(01) 668866
	The Old School House, Eblana Ave, Dun Laoghaire, Co Dublin	.	(01) 2808777

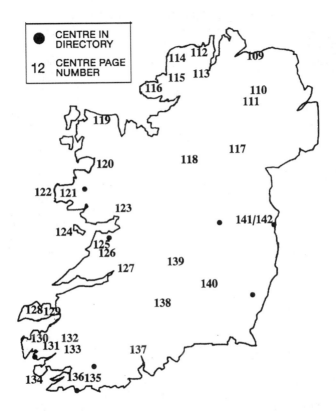

All phone numbers are given with their regional code in Ireland. To phone form the UK dial 00 353 followed by the local code (missing of the first 0) and number.

CAUSEWAY COAST HOSTEL

4 Victoria Terrace
Atlantic Circle
Portstewart
Co Derry

Causeway Coast Hostel is a cosy, people-friendly place for individuals, families and groups. It is set in Portstewart, a small seaside town on the north coast of Ireland, with a harbour at one end and two miles of sandy beach at the other. The hostel is 50 yards from the ocean and close to shops and pubs, although with an open fire and music in the common room it can prove a struggle to drag yourself out at night. It is definitely worth struggling out to see the unique Giants Causeway, Dunluce Castle, Bushmills Whiskey Distillery and (for those with a head for heights) Carrick-A-Rede rope bridge. The hostel can arrange or provide information about :- spectacular coastal walks, cycle tours, scuba diving, horse riding, golf, bird watching, boat hire and fishing.

TELEPHONE CONTACT Rick UK (01265) 833789
OPENING SEASON All year
OPENING HOURS All day access, no night-time curfew
NUMBER OF BEDS 28
BOOKING REQUIREMENTS Not essential but recommended during high season. Phone/postal bookings, normally no deposit.
PRICE PER NIGHT £6 per person

DIRECTIONS GR 816387. The hostel is 100yds from the A2 road on the eastern edge of town. Take turn signposted for Portmore Bay Hotel. Trains from Derry/Belfast to Coleraine (nearest station). Direct buses from Belfast/Dublin/Derry and Coleraine go to Atlantic Circle stop 100yds from hostel.

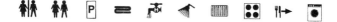

GORTIN OUTDOOR CENTRE
Glenpark Road
Gortin, Omagh
Co Tyrone

Gortin Outdoor Centre is an old school which has been converted to a self catering hostel. There are three bedrooms each with 6 bunks, and the open plan kitchen/living/dining area allows ample room for an evening chat around the fire. There is also a drying room and showers with hot water.

Gortin village is on your doorstep and has a wide variety of pubs and shops. It is a picturesque village set in the heart of the extremely attractive Sperrin Mountains, within walking distance of the Ulster Way. A bus can take you to the Ulster History Park and the Ulster American Folk Park is also in the vicinity. This is an ideal area for walking and cycling and you can hire our bikes to explore. Fishing, canoeing, pony riding and nature trails are also near at hand.

TELEPHONE CONTACT Joan Hempton UK (01662) 648770 / 648083
OPENING SEASON July to Sept (inc) for individuals, open all year for groups.
OPENING HOURS 9am to 10.30pm
NUMBER OF BEDS 18
BOOKING REQUIREMENTS Booking required (£50 deposit rquired for group bookings.)
PRICE PER NIGHT £6 per person. Phone for group rates.

DIRECTIONS The hostel is 50 metres from the cross roads in Gortin Village. Gortin is 10 miles north west of Omagh.

OMAGH INDEPENDENT HOSTEL

9a Waterworks Road
Omagh , Co Tyrone
BT79 7JS

We are a small family run hostel, nestling at the edge of the Sperrin Mountains. Billy and Marella Fyffe with their children and sundry dogs etc, look forward to having you to stay. This new hostel, has 29 beds, the rooms are of varying sizes sleeping from 1 to 7 people. We have all the usual facilities (check out the symbol chart below), we also have a large conservatory area for relaxing in, an out door play area where children can play in safety, and an unbelievable panoramic view of the Northern Irish country side ! We positively encourage families, disabled people, dog owners and any other minority group, as well as the usual mainstream folk. The hostel is convenient to the Ulster American Folk Park (4 miles), The Ulster History Park (5 miles) and we are 2 miles from the Ulster Way. Megalithic sites abound in this area.

TELEPHONE/FAX CONTACT Marella & Billy (01662)241973
OPENING SEASON All year
OPENING HOURS All day, please arrive before 10pm on first night.
NUMBER OF BEDS 29
BOOKING REQUIREMENTS Pre-booking essential for groups one month in advance, deposit required.
PRICE PER NIGHT £6 per adult, £5 if under 18 years of age.

DIRECTIONS From Omagh take B48 towards Gortin. turn right onto Killybrack Road before Charles Hurst garage. Keep on road and follow signs to hostel.

BUNNATON HOSTEL

Bunnaton
Glenvar
Letterkenny
Co Donegal

On the banks of Lough Swilly "Bunnaton Hostel" must have one of the most spectacular settings of any hostel. Built originally as a coastguard station circa 1830 and run as an An Oige Hostel from 1938 to 1985. It had fallen into disrepair when it was purchased by Anne and Chris Hewett in 1988 and is now up and running again as a very popular independent hostel with a friendly and informal atmosphere about it. The Knockalla Mountains are well worth the hike to the top and the view must surely be unsurpassed in all of Ireland. For an *away from it all break*, far from the hustle and bustle of the more promoted tourist areas, go north to "Bunnaton Hostel" on the Fanad Peninsula, one of the few remaining areas of unspoilt rural Ireland.

TELEPHONE CONTACT (074) 50122 Anne
OPENING SEASON All year
OPENING HOURS All day
NUMBER OF BEDS 25
BOOKING REQUIREMENTS Booking is required in July and August, but there are occasionally spare beds.
PRICE PER NIGHT IR£6 (dorm) IR£7.50 (private room), Group rates available on application.

DIRECTIONS We are 20 miles North of Letterkenny on the Fanad Scenic Drive. Take the Ramelton (Rathmelton) road from Letterkenny and at Ramelton you can either take the Rathmullen road to Bunnaton or go via Kerrykeel (Carrowkeel) through Glenvar to Bunnaton.

FINN FARM
Cappry
Ballybofey
Co. Donegal

Open fires! Irish traditional music! Self contained kitchen!
Camping! Free showers, comfortable beds and a homely
atmosphere.

Eddy the owner will have time to guide you from the megalithic
age to the pleasures of modern rural Ireland.

Riding instruction is available for the novice or you may wish to
hack out for a few hours - or trail ride for two days or a week
through forest, hills and valley.

You may go hill walking on the Ulster Way or spend a day in the
local leisure centre with its jaccusi, steam room, sauna, gym and
22 meter pool. *You will have fun !*

TELEPHONE CONTACT Eddy Gallagher (074) 32261
OPENING SEASON All Year
OPENING HOURS All hours
NUMBER OF BEDS 20
BOOKING REQUIREMENTS Booking is optional.
PRICE PER NIGHT From IR £5

DIRECTIONS From Ballybofey take Glenties Road for 3 km -
Turn left at hostel sign where you will see a big house at top of
lane. The dog is friendly.

GREENE'S HOLIDAY HOSTEL
Carnmore Road
Dungloe, Co Donegal

Dungloe is a small friendly town surrounded by countryside, from where the visitor can tour the whole of Donegal. Here you can explore a beautiful, wild, rugged region of mountains, lakes and sea, in an atmosphere of peace and tranquillity far removed from the hustle and bustle of urban areas. The area has many amenities to offer, miles of golden sandy, safe beaches, golf courses, excellent angling facilities, mountain climbing, scenic walks and drives. You may visit the off-shore islands of Arranmore and Tory, or, spend a day in Glenveagh National Park or at the Dunlewey Heritage Centre.

Greene's Holiday Hostel provides self catering accommodation 500m from the town centre of Dungloe. The hostel is fully heated and sleeping accommodation is in private rooms or dormitories. Hot showers, a drying room and laundry are provided. The hostels is local to a leisure centre, shops, and pubs with music. You can hire bikes at the hostel.

TELEPHONE CONTACT (075) 21021
OPENING SEASON All year
OPENING HOURS Flexible
NUMBER OF BEDS 38
BOOKING REQUIREMENTS Book ahead in high season.
PRICE PER NIGHT IR£6 (dorms),   IR£7 (private room). Please enquire for group rates.

DIRECTIONS Private bus service daily from Dublin, Galway, Larn/Antrim to Dungloe, phone us for times. As you enter Dungloe our hostel is at Greene's Corner beside main junction to Glenties and Gweedore, follow camping park sign.

CAMPBELL'S HOLIDAY HOSTEL
Main Street
Glenties
Co Donegal

Campbell's Holiday Hostel is situated in the centre of 'Ireland's Tidiest Town'. It is spacious, modern and clean, and has central heating and laundry machines. There are rooms of two, four and six beds.

The hostel is ideal as a base for touring County Donegal as it is in the centre of the county. It is also ideal for hill walking in the Blue Stack Mountains and Aghla Hills. The excellent Owenea River, with salmon and sea trout, flows along the rear of the hostel, and it is only 10km to the beach at Portnoo. Horse riding and golf are available within 10km of the hostel. Glenties is famous for the 'Fiddlers Weekend' which is the last weekend in September, and throughout the year there is music three nights a week in the local pub.

TELEPHONE CONTACT (075) 51491
OPENING SEASON 1st March to 31st October
OPENING HOURS 24 hours
NUMBER OF BEDS 36
BOOKING REQUIREMENTS Booking is essential for groups and advisable for individuals in July and August.
PRICE PER NIGHT From IR£5.00 per person (sharing)

DIRECTIONS The hostel is on the main road from Giants Causeway to Slieve League (Donegal to Dungloe road), 16m north of Donegal, 25m west of Letterkenny. Bus from Dublin.

DÚN ULÚN HOUSE
Kilcar
Co Donegal

This luxurious Hostel consists of ten bedrooms, all of which have their own shower, toilet and handbasin. The house is centrally heated with full modern kitchen facilities and separate dining room. There is also a lounge with open fire and TV. Situated in South West Donegal, the hostel has spectacular views and a glorious setting overlooking Towney and Donegal Bay with counties Leitrim, Sligo and Mayo in view.

A perfect base for touring this beautiful area of Donegal only a few miles from the highest sea cliffs in Europe "Sliabh Liag". It is an ideal location for outdoor enthusiasts, for fishing swimming, walking, mountain climbing, boat trips, deep sea angling, cycling (hire bikes at the hostel) and horse riding. Home of traditional music and crafts.

TELEPHONE CONTACT (073) 38137
OPENING SEASON All year (except 24 & 25 Dec)
OPENING HOURS 8am to 12.30pm
NUMBER OF BEDS 38
BOOKING REQUIREMENTS Book ahead (normally minimum of 7 days notice) in July, August and bank holiday weekends. Deposit required.
PRICE PER NIGHT From IR£5 (sharing). B&B from IR£12.50 (sharing). Suitable for groups, one leader free per 12 persons.

DIRECTIONS Leaving Killybegs, go to Kilcar village, through village on coast road to Carrick and Glencolmkille. The hostel is the first large house on right at top of hill, 1km from village.

SANDVILLE HOUSE HOSTEL

Ballyconnell
Co Cavan

One of Ireland's original independent hostels, Sandville House offers spacious, well equipped accommodation in a stone barn. Peaceful and private space is available for groups and retreats, and we have acres of garden for children (and others!) to play. You'll find easy access to our loveliest and least-spoilt lakes (rent a canoe!) and to the gorgeous, empty hills of West Cavan and Fermanagh. Borrow a bike to head for the local bar, or just put your feet up in front of the fire. Camp in the field if you prefer. Double rooms no extra charge to first comers. So when you've had enough of the coast, head inland, you'll be glad you came!

Within easy reach: Marble Arch caves, the Carvan Way, Lough Erne, the Shannon-Erne Waterway and the towns of Cavan and Enniskillen.

Groups Welcome; call us if you need help with activity planning or catering !

TELEPHONE CONTACT (049) 26297
OPENING SEASON All year (but phone ahead in winter)
OPENING HOURS 24 hours. No new arrivals after midnight.
NUMBER OF BEDS 20 (larger groups by arrangement)
BOOKING REQUIREMENTS Groups should book ahead.
PRICE PER NIGHT IR£5.00 per person. Groups (10+) IR£4.00 per person, or hire whole barn IR£80.

DIRECTIONS Signed off main Dublin road 2 miles from Ballyconnell. Dublin-Enniskillen-Donegal bus stops in Ballyconnell town (phone for pick-up).

TOWN CLOCK HOSTEL
Town Centre
Carrick-on-Shannon
Co Leitrim

Carrick-on-Shannon is Ireland's loveliest inland resort, with landscaped river banks, busy marina, canoeing, watersports, walks and fishing stands. Adjacent to hill walking in lovely Leitrim and Rosscommon. There are 41 lakes within 6 miles and 14 pubs (some with darts and music) within five minutes walk. Other amenities are, in season, heated outdoor swimming pool, sports complex, 9 hole golf course, launderette, good restaurants and take away foods.

The Town Clock Hostel is a 14 bed hostel in a picturesque courtyard, with patio tables. Parking available for small minibuses, cars and bikes and bike hire is available . Fully equipped kitchen, 2 mixed dorms, family room, heated common room, hot water and clothes line. Special schools welcome.

TELEPHONE CONTACT Breda Dunne (078) 20068
OPENING SEASON 1st June-30th Sept, Groups 1st Feb-1st Dec
OPENING HOURS No curfew. Hostel closed for cleaning 11am-12pm. Hostelers leaving, please do so by 11am.
NUMBER OF BEDS 14
BOOKING REQUIREMENTS Phone booking advised July and August, beds held to 6pm. Groups advised to book.
PRICE PER NIGHT IR£5.50 per person. Groups of 8+ get 10% discount (except in July and Aug). IR£65 per night sole use.

DIRECTIONS Carrick-on-Shannon is on the N4 from Dublin. Trains and buses from Dublin to Sligo call at the town. From Belfast take M1 and A4 then R207. The Hostel is in the town centre under the arch by the town clock.

KILCOMMON LODGE
Pullathomas/Ballina
Co Mayo

Kilcommon Lodge is located on the coastline of North West Mayoina in a village adjacent to the sea. The house is surrounded by gardens with old trees, it is close to rivers, lake, hills, cliffs and beautiful sandy beaches. There is a ferry crossing Sruwaddacon Bay and a fisher boat will take day trips from the Mullet Peninsula to the Island of Innishkea. Kilcommon Lodge is the starting point for visiting archaeological sites, ceide fields, a sculptor trail and is ideal for bird watching. The area is not spoiled by tourism. With its small fishing ports, boglands and valleys it is the place for peace and relaxation.

Kilcommon Lodge offers comfortable dorms and private rooms with H&C, central heating, hot showers, a well equipped self-catering kitchen and cosy common room with turf fire and library. Meals (inc vegetarian) can be provided for individuals and groups.

TELEPHONE CONTACT Betty or Fritz (097) 84621
OPENING SEASON Closed from 15th Jan to 15th March.
OPENING HOURS All day
NUMBER OF BEDS 20
BOOKING REQUIREMENTS Groups should book four weeks in advance with deposit.
PRICE PER NIGHT IR£5.50 (dorm) IR£6.50 (private room) per person. Please enquire for group rates.

DIRECTIONS Ballina-Bangor-Glenamoy-Pullathomas. Ballina-Killala-Ballycastle-Glenamoy-Pullatomas. Westport-Mulranny-Bangor-Glenamoy-Pullthomas. Mc Grath buses provide a service from Ballina to Hostel.

CLUB
ATLANTIC
Altamount Street
Westport
Co Mayo

The Town of Westport is situated on the beautiful island studded Clew Bay, and resting in the Shadow of towering Croagh Patrick. The town has everything a traveller needs, fabulous pubs, excellent restaurants, great shops and a super atmosphere! Local amenities include organised walking routes and hill climbing, horse riding, beautiful sandy beaches, sailing and canoeing, deep sea angling, historical and archaeological tours. Westport is an ideal base to tour Achill Island and Connemara.

Club Atlantic is a large modern clean hostel with lots of twin and family rooms (bring your own sheets), many with en-suite facilities. The Hostel is very well equipped with excellent self catering kitchen, laundry and drying facilities, free hot showers, TV room and games rooms. The Croagh Patrick Exhibition, which interprets the Holy Mountain and encourages the viewer to experience the pleasure of a climb, is on view in the hostel and free to guests.

TELEPHONE CONTACT Anne or Olive (098) 26644
OPENING SEASON 3rd March to 31st Oct Inclusive
OPENING HOURS All day
NUMBER OF BEDS 140
BOOKING REQUIREMENTS Booking is not essential but it helps ! Deposit required with group bookings.
PRICE PER NIGHT From IR£5.50

DIRECTIONS Westport is served several times daily with trains and buses and on the national routes. The hostel is opposite the train station, 5 minutes walk from the town centre.

THE OLD MONASTERY
Letterfrack
Connemara
Co Galway

The Old Monastery is a spacious Georgian House, converted to a modern and comfortable hostel. Accommodation is in private and family rooms, the common areas have turf fires and a laundry service is available. A light breakfast is provided free of charge and a vegetarian feast is served every night in The Monastery Cafe.

The Old Monastery is adjacent to Connemara National Park and the Twelve Bens. It is a short spin away from the sea, the sandy beaches of Renvyle, Killary Harbour and the Island of Inishbofin. The hostel provides a bike hire service. Letterfrack village is a popular spot for musicians throughout the year.

TELEPHONE CONTACT (095) 41132 Stephen
OPENING SEASON All year
OPENING HOURS 9am to 6pm (no curfew)
NUMBER OF BEDS 50
BOOKING REQUIREMENTS Booking is advised.
PRICE PER NIGHT From IR£6.50 to IR£8.00 , free breakfast.

DIRECTIONS Letterfrack is on the (N59) Galway - Clifden - Westport road, 9 miles north of Clifden. The Hostel is beside the church in the village

INISHBOFIN ISLAND HOSTEL
Inishbofin
Co Galway

Inishbofin Island Hostel still retains the character and charm of a traditional farmhouse although it has been converted into a modern hostel. The hostel has 38 beds with duvets provided (sheets can be rented), full kitchen facilities, central heating and free shower. The large conservatory offers spectacular views of the Connemara mountains and coastline and the hostel is 500m from the pub where there are excellent Irish music sessions. Inishbofin is one of Ireland's most westerly islands. It is situated 11kms off Cleggan Town in Connemara and is 5.5kms long, 3km wide with a population of approx 200. The island has magnificent sandy beaches which are safe for swimming, monastic ruins, a Cromwellian fort, two hotels, pub, restaurant, post office and a few small grocery shops. There is a wide variety of sea, bird and plant life including grey seals and the rare Corncrake, and the seas are ideal for anglers and scuba divers.

TELEPHONE/FAX CONTACT (095) 45855 fax 45803
OPENING SEASON 1 Aprill to 1st November (Inc)
OPENING HOURS All day
NUMBER OF BEDS 38
BOOKING REQUIREMENTS Booking is not essential but is strongly advised in July, August and bank holiday weekends. Deposit required as soon as possible after booking.
PRICE PER NIGHT IR£5.50 (dorm) IR£8 (private room).

DIRECTIONS All ferries leave from Cleggan Pier. Turn right when you leave the ferry, take road to east end of village. Hostel is on the left after approximately 700 meters.

GALWAY CITY HOSTEL

25-27 Dominick Street Lower
Galway
Co Galway

The Galway City Hostel has a very relaxed way of looking at things. We have free entertainment from juggling to acoustic guitar sessions all provided by staff, guests and some very interesting locals. Our facilities include, self catering kitchen, safe bicycle area, laundry service, luggage room and showers. We have four dormitories, two rooms of eight and two rooms of twelve. One rooms is reserved for females.

Local attractions are numerous, Galway is a city that can interest anyone and there are many pubs with all types of music within 2 minutes walk of the hostel. Our staff are more than willing to help with any problems or queries that guests may have during their stay. We have guests from all over the world stay here again and again. To quote one of our guests "this is one of the best hostels I have ever stayed in".

TELEPHONE CONTACT Ciran or Eilis (091) 566267
OPENING SEASON All year
OPENING HOURS Summer 7am-3.30am, low season 8am-3am
NUMBER OF BEDS 42
BOOKING REQUIREMENTS Booking is recommended for high season and weekends. Send deposit (min £15) for groups.
PRICE PER NIGHT IR£5.50 low season, IR£6.50 high season.

DIRECTIONS From the rail/bus station go to the top left corner of Eyre Square. Turn left and go down Shop Street and over O'Briens Bridge (300m). Turn left after the bridge onto Dominick Street and our hostel is the last building on the right. A big yellow and red hostel ! The above takes about 5 minutes.

MAINISTIR HOUSE HOSTEL
Mainister
Inismór
Co Galway

Mainister House, built on a landscape of barren rock overlooking Galway Bay, is situated on the outskirts of the little bustling village of Cill Ronáin and within short walking distance of the harbour. A simple whitewashed hostel on the edge of the atlantic, Mainistir House offers you all the comforts of a guesthouse, with small dorms and private rooms, at the low economy rate of a hostel.

Self catering facilities are available, but Joel is a natural in the kitchen and creates a vaguely vegetarian buffet every evening which is imaginative, nourishing and good value. You can bring your own wine and chat at the long tables with the cosmopolitan hostellers, while Joel weaves in and out touching everyone with his infectious enthusiasm.

TELEPHONE CONTACT Sinead or Joel (099) 61169
OPENING SEASON All year
OPENING HOURS 24 hours
NUMBER OF BEDS 78
BOOKING REQUIREMENTS Booking with 25% deposit is essential during summer months.
PRICE PER NIGHT IR£7.50 per person. Group rates available.

DIRECTIONS The hostel is 1km from the pier in Cill Ronáin heading towards Dun Aengus Fort. The hostel runs a minibus from the pier to the hostel for £1 per person.

KINCORA HOUSE & THE BURREN HOLIDAY HOSTEL

Lisdoonvarna
Co Clare

Owned and supervised by the Drennan family, Kincora House is a beautiful old mansion built in 1879 and is the perfect location for a holiday in the spectacular Burren region. The building houses a traditional pub and restaurant where excellent food is served at reasonable prices, and traditional music and dancing can be appreciated on selected evenings though the season. The hostel has 60 beds, mainly in four bedded rooms and we have double rooms for couples. There is a large self catering kitchen.

The Burren has a landscape unlike any other in Europe, and once visited people return time and time again to experience its atmosphere, its people, and its music. Idyllic walking and cycle routes are here to be enjoyed and the area is rich in rare wildflowers. Nearby are the Cliffs of Moher, Polnabrone Dolman which dates back to 4000 BC and the Aran Islands.

TELEPHONE CONTACT Doreen Drennan (065) 74300
OPENING SEASON All year
OPENING HOURS 7am to time required (no curfew).
NUMBER OF BEDS 60
BOOKING REQUIREMENTS Booking is advisable, deposit required for individuals in July, August September and bank holiday weekends and for groups thoughout the year.
PRICE PER NIGHT IR£6.50 per person. Group rates available.

DIRECTIONS From Lisdoonvarna town centre take the road which displays an Esso sign at garage, proceed to first T junction. The Hostel is a three story building on this junction (5 mins walk from town centre).

BOGHILL CENTRE
Boghill
Kilfenora
Co Clare

The Boghill Centre is situated at the edge of the Burren, just two miles from Lisdoonvarna and three and half miles from Kilfenora where regular music sessions are held. Set in 50 acres of protected bogland it is secluded and private and offers quiet walks both on its own grounds and down country lanes.

The centre is owned and run by musicians. We conduct traditional music work shops thoughout the summer, Christmas and during the New Year. We are open all year to accommodate groups and individuals. Diverse activities can be arranged by us to suit you. The area is ideal for cycling, walking and horse riding. Bikes can be hired locally and there are several riding stables nearby. Groups are welcome to use all the facilities of the centre and to organise their own events. Comfortable accommodation and delicious food create a relaxing atmosphere.

TELEPHONE CONTACT Sonja O'Brien (065) 74644
OPENING SEASON All year
OPENING HOURS 24 hours
NUMBER OF BEDS 28
BOOKING REQUIREMENTS Booking is essential for group bookings.
PRICE PER NIGHT IR£7 per person

DIRECTIONS   From Lisdoonvarna take the main road to Kilfenora. Take the second turning to the right - about 1½ miles and on a bad bend. Then take the first turning to the left - about 60 yds. Boghill centre will be the first building on the road.

CLYDE HOUSE
St Alphonsus Street
Limerick
Co Limerick

Limerick is noted for spontaneous sing songs and traditional music. There are many theme or character pubs in the city that help to create the right atmosphere for all to join in the chorus and the Guinness is good everywhere. Entertainment to suit all tastes is available at pubs and theatres and there are excellent riverside walks. Bunratty Castle and folk park are just a few miles away. Limerick City is the ideal base from which to tour the many attractions of the Shannon Region.

Clyde House is a luxurious hostel complex with self catering en-suite rooms and dormitories with colour TV. Amenities include Bureau de Change, credit card facilities, large private car and bicycle park, breakfast room and coffee shop, launderette, games and recreation rooms. There is a resident house manager and security monitoring throughout. Group bookings are welcomed and lunch and dinner requirements can be arranged if requested.

TELEPHONE CONTACT (061) 314357 / 314727
OPENING SEASON All year
OPENING HOURS Flexible
NUMBER OF BEDS 127
BOOKING REQUIREMENTS Pre-booking required for groups with 25% deposit.
PRICE PER NIGHT IR£7.50 in dorm, higher prices for single and twin rooms. Special group rates available.

DIRECTIONS Go to the top of O'Connell street, past monument, turn right at next traffic lights and come down Gerard Street. Clyde house is directly in front of you, just off Henry Street.

LYNCHS
CASTLEGREGORY
HOSTEL

Opposite the Church
Castlegregory Village
Co Kerry

This friendly hostel is situated directly across the street from Castlegregory village church. The village has seven pubs, all a short walk away, which provide Irish music and songs. The family run hostel is **always** attended by the husband and wife and all visitors are made to feel at home by the proprietors who chat and drink coffee with them.

There are no extra charges for electricity, heating or showers. Self-catering facilities are provided again at no extra charge. There is no night-time curfew and hostellers are welcome to arrive at any time of day. Blankets/duvets and pillows are provided and towels and sheets can be hired for a minimal fee. The hostel is very warm cosy and comfortable.

TELEPHONE CONTACT Mr and Mrs Lynch (066) 39128
OPENING SEASON All year
OPENING HOURS 24 hr service
NUMBER OF BEDS 20
BOOKING REQUIREMENTS Booking not required.
PRICE PER NIGHT IR£6 per person. Group rates available for six or more people, please enquire.

DIRECTIONS Castlegregory is on the R560 between Tralee and Dingle. Buses from Tralee to Dingle pass through the village. The hostel is directly across the street from the Village church.

BOG VIEW HOSTEL

Lougher
Inch
Annascaul
Co Kerry

Bog View Hostel is small friendly and cosy. We have a large dining/sitting room with an open turf fire which is always alight. There is no shortage of showers and hot water is available all day long. Accommodation is provided in dorms or private rooms and our large garden offers opportunities for outdoor games. John and Susan offer you lots of good friendly Irish hospitality. We will also cook meals for you if we have advance notice.

The area has a lot to offer. The famous Inch Strand, a 5km sand bar pushing out into Dingle Bay, is a must to visit. There is lots of hill walking in the area and Annascaul Lake is an ideal location for a tranquil mountain walk. Wind surfing, fishing and plenty of Irish music are available on the Dingle Peninsular during the summer months. The bus stops outside the hostel and we may be able to pick you up from the nearby village.

TELEPHONE/FAX CONTACT John or Susan Tel (066) 58125 Fax (066) 23870
OPENING SEASON 1st May to 31st October
OPENING HOURS All day
NUMBER OF BEDS 24
BOOKING REQUIREMENTS 50% deposit is needed to book.
PRICE PER NIGHT IR£6 per person

DIRECTIONS On the main Tralee/Dingle road 8km from Camp village and 7km from Annascaul village, 5km from Inch village. Tralee/Dingle bus stops outside hostel

THE RING LYNE
Chapeltown
Valentia Island
Co Kerry

The Ring Lyne hostel is a former guest house located in an old village at the heart of Valentia Island. We offer hostel accommodation and en-suite B&B, all in well furnished bedrooms with h/c washbasins. We have a modern kitchen and bar food is served all day (steaks and seafood a speciality) in our fully licensed bar. Valentia, although an island in its sense of remoteness and the character of its people, is accessible from the Ring of Kerry by road bridge and passenger ferry. The island has a rich history with prehistoric standing stones (Ogham Stones), wedge tombs and beehive huts. At Glanleam Gardens tropical plants imported over a century ago have run riot in the island's mild climate and now provide a profusion of shelter, colour and perfume. You can swim at Glanleam beach and angling offers over 30 species of fish. Take a boat trip to Skellig Michael and visit the worlds finest example of early christian architecture with 1,400 year old stone built cells, oratories, terraces and stairways.

TELEPHONE CONTACT Frances or Sean (066) 76103
OPENING SEASON All year
OPENING HOURS All day
NUMBER OF BEDS 22
BOOKING REQUIREMENTS Booking is not essential but could be useful. Please book a week in advance (20% deposit).
PRICE PER NIGHT IR£6.50 per person, groups of 10 or more IR£5.50 (prices inc shower). B&B en-suite also available.

DIRECTIONS The hostel is in the centre of Chapeltown which is 2 miles from the road bridge on to the island of Valentia and 3 miles from the Knightstown passenger ferry(summer only).

CLIMBERS INN
Glencar
Co Kerry

This hostel is undergoing renovation work to be completed in March 96.

Climbers Inn, in the heart of Ireland's highest mountain range, was established in 1879 and is now run by the families' 4th generation, Johnny Walsh. It is the type of pub/hostel where locals and travellers will chat around the open turf fire and enjoy a pint of Guinness. The hostel has beds for 27-30 people in en-suite rooms of 2,4,6 and 8 beds. It is heated with drying room, laundry room, hot showers and cooking facilities. We have a shop and post office which stocks provisions and has Bureau de Change and tourist information services. In addition to the dormitory accommodation the Climbers Inn also provides B&B and camping. There is home cooked food from IR£4.95 (inc vegetarian dishes) in the pub and packed lunches can be provided. The hostel in on the Kerry Way in an area ideal for climbing, hill walking and salmon and trout fishing (licences available at the post office). Bikes are available for hire and, with advanced notice, day and weekend courses can be arranged in field studies, climbing, sailing, orienteering and climbing. This is the real hidden Ireland where you meet the people, not just travellers.

TELEPHONE/FAX CONTACT (066) 60101 fax 60104
OPENING SEASON All year (Except Xmas Day)
OPENING HOURS 24 hr access. Service from 9am to 11pm.
NUMBER OF BEDS 30
BOOKING REQUIREMENTS Book in advance in summer.
PRICE PER NIGHT IR£9.50 - 13.50 with continental breakfast.

DIRECTIONS GR 841 724. Buses from Killarney (16 miles), rail station to Killorglin, then 9 miles along Glencar Rd.

FOSSA HOLIDAY HOSTEL
Fossa
Killarney
Co Kerry

Fossa Holiday Hostel is situated in the village of Fossa, close to the lakes and mountains of Killarney. Within the area there is Killarney National Park which provides some beautiful scenic walks and cycling paths near the lake and forest. Fossa is only 7 miles from Carrantuohill (Ireland's highest mountains) and the Macgillycuddy Reeks. Fishing on the River Laune, golf on two championship courses and horse riding are all available locally.

The hostel has its own self catering kitchen and dining room. On site facilites include shop (Easter to Sept), restaurant and take away (June to Aug), children's playground, tennis court, TV and games room, laundry and cycle hire. Tours can be arranged. There is ample car and coach parking outside the hostel. We can cater for all types of groups providing self catering, B&B or half board. Fossa Holiday Hostel is a member of the I.H.H.

TELEPHONE CONTACT (064) 31497 Derry/Nina
OPENING SEASON 13th March 1996 to 31st October 1996
OPENING HOURS All day access - no curfew
NUMBER OF BEDS 40
BOOKING REQUIREMENTS Individuals are advised to book in July and August. Booking is essential for groups. Deposit required.
PRICE PER NIGHT From IR£5.50, group rates available on request.

DIRECTIONS Fossa Holiday Hostel is located 5km west of Killarney town centre on the main Ring of Kerry/Killorglin Road (R562). There is a Texaco filling station outside the complex which includes a caravan and camping park.

ATLAS HOUSE BUDGET ACCOMMODATION

The Park
Park Road
Killarney
Co Kerry

Situated in Killarney in the beautiful south west of Ireland, Atlas House is a brand new, purpose built hostel. It is reasonably priced and exceptionally comfortable with dormitory accommodation and private rooms available. Atlas House also has a luxurious TV lounge with satellite TV, self catering kitchen, dining room, meeting room and ample parking at rear of building.

Atlas House is ideally located for exploring the magnificent lakes of Killarney, Muckross House and Gardens, the Gap of Dunloe, Ring of Kerry and Dingle Peninsula. Tours for these can be arranged at reception. Bike hire on site. Killarney is ideal for hill walking, golfing, fishing, horse riding and many other activities. Our friendly staff are always on hand to arrange these and to assist in making your stay a most enjoyable one.

TELEPHONE CONTACT   Tim O'Donoghue (064) 36144
OPENING SEASON All year
OPENING HOURS Open all day, no curfew
NUMBER OF BEDS 140
BOOKING REQUIREMENTS   Not essential but highly recommended
PRICE PER NIGHT IR£7.50 per person. Group discounts.

DIRECTIONS   Turn right out of railway/bus station. Follow signpost marked Cork. Walk for 5 mins and take first left at traffic light and the hostel is just there on the right hand side.

GARRANES FARMHOUSE HOSTEL
Cahermore, Beara
West Cork

No one who visits Garranes comes away unmarked by its dramatic beauty. From the majestic setting on cliffs high above the Atlantic Ocean, views unfold across the shimmering surface of Bantry Bay, and along one of Europe's last unspoiled stretches of coastline. Here is nature at her most untamed, raw and magical. The hostel is an old farmhouse providing a homely atmosphere, comfortable accommodation and excellent facilities. Garranes is an ideal base for walking, cycling, and for visits to Dursey Island, Allihies, Dunboy Castle and Bere Island. The hostel is next to Dzogchan Beara, an internationally renowned Tibetan Buddhist Retreat Centre where introductory meditation classes, courses and retreats of variable duration, take place throughout the year. Limited provisions are available at Cahermore post office (2½miles). Plenty of shops in Castletownbere. A warm and friendly welcome awaits you.

TELEPHONE CONTACT Andrew Warr (027) 73147
OPENING SEASON All year
OPENING HOURS All day
NUMBER OF BEDS 20
BOOKING REQUIREMENTS For family room & high season.
PRICE PER NIGHT IR£6.00 (dorm) IR£8.00 (double room) per person. Please enquire for family rates.

DIRECTIONS 5 miles west of Castletownbere on the R572 to Allihies, there is a track signposted to hostel and Retreat Centre, follow for ½ mile to end. Private bus service to Castletownbere from Cork, Bantry and Glengarriff and similar bus from Killarney and Kenmare to Castletownbere (phone hostel for details).

SHIPLAKE MOUNTAIN HOSTEL

Shiplake
Dunmanway
Co Cork

Stay in a traditional homely farmhouse with all hostel comforts like self catering kitchen, hot showers, cosy common room with a stove, spacious dormitories. Spend your night privately in one of the gypsy barrel-top caravans or pitch your tent in the big garden. Nestle with us in this superb setting on the side of a hill viewing onto the foothills of the Shehy Mountains. Enjoy the friendly and welcoming atmosphere, delicious vegetarian cooking, homemade products, organic vegetables. There are excellent walks, cycles and swims in this unspoilt rural and mountainous area. We are situated in the centre of West Cork and there is a big variety of sites of interest. Castles, stone circles, nature reserve, nice beaches, all in easy reach. We offer a peaceful and relaxing haven for singles, couples and families alike and a free pub run to one of the local music pubs in the evening.

TELEPHONE/FAX CONTACT (023) 45750 Uli
OPENING SEASON All year
OPENING HOURS All day and night
NUMBER OF BEDS 20
BOOKING REQUIREMENTS Booking is essential in high season, especially for private rooms. 20% deposit .
PRICE PER NIGHT IR£5.50 (dorm), IR£7.00 (private room) Group rates IR£5.

DIRECTIONS From Dunmanway, take Castle Road next to 'Market Diner House'. Follow road for 5km/3miles out of town in the direction of Coolkelure. Look for hostel sign on right.

HARBOUR VIEW
SMALL INDEPENDENT HOSTEL

Harbour View
Bantry
Co Cork

For weary travellers this scenic haven is the perfect location to explore the tranquil beauty of Bantry Bay steeped in history and folklore. A warm welcome awaits you.

Overlooking the harbour the hostel has three dorms and private rooms. Fully equipped self- catering kitchen, hot showers, dining area and TV. Bedding and linen are provided free of charge.

Available locally is bicycle hire, car hire, boat hire, sailing, fishing, golf, horse riding.

The hostel is within five minutes walk of the bus stop, Tourist Information Office, shops, restaurants, post office and pubs with traditional Irish music and "crack galore".

TELEPHONE CONTACT Kevin Barry (027) 51140
OPENING SEASON All year
OPENING HOURS 24 hours
NUMBER OF BEDS 35
BOOKING REQUIREMENTS Not required
PRICE PER NIGHT IR£5.50 per person

DIRECTIONS The hostel is in the town square, beside the bus stop. It overlooks Bantry Harbour.

CORK CITY
INDEPENDENT HOSTEL

100 Lower Glanmire Road
Cork City
Co Cork

You will find our relaxed hostel only 5-10 minutes walk from the city centre and 200yds from the train station. We have all the facilities you need. Hot showers 24 hours a day, kitchen with free tea and coffee and a cosy common room. We also have a television and video room with an open fire for the rainy days and on sunny days you can hang-out in our lovely back yard for a tan. We have a free map of Cork to start you off on your adventures.

The house has mainly double or twin rooms, there are some dormitories with 4 beds and one with 6 beds. The appealing atmosphere of our place is due to our love for candlelight, music, original decor and most important of all, our helpful and welcoming staff.

TELEPHONE CONTACT (021) 509089 Jeremy
OPENING SEASON All year
OPENING HOURS All day
NUMBER OF BEDS 25
BOOKING REQUIREMENTS In high season book one day before arrival, no deposit required.
PRICE PER NIGHT IR£6 (dorms) or IR£7 for private double room.

DIRECTIONS Coming out of train station turn right, hostel is 200yds on the left hand side. Coming from bus station, cross the bridge, turn second right towards train station, hostel is on left.

CASHEL HOLIDAY HOSTEL

6 St John Street
Cashel
Co Tipperary

Cashel Holiday Hostel is a well established accommodation base in the centre of Medieval Cashel. The hostel is a 200 year old Georgian house and has been highly recommended by the leading accommodation guide books. Our accommodation rooms have 4-6 beds and there is also a number of double rooms which are all brightly decorated, spotlessly clean and extremely spacious. The kitchen is self catering with all the mod cons of a modern kitchen and it is kept very clean. Above all this hostel prides itself on a great atmosphere and friendly staff.

Cashel, originally the Fort of Munster, was once the capital of this southern province. The outcrop of rock, rearing above the plain, dominates the land routes and in times of old the southward bound Kings of Ireland would come to this spot.
Follow the Kings, come to Cashel.

TELEPHONE CONTACT P J Quinlan (062) 62330
OPENING SEASON All year
OPENING HOURS All day
NUMBER OF BEDS 44
BOOKING REQUIREMENTS Booking is advisable
PRICE PER NIGHT Dorms IR£6, Double room IR£8.50 per person (reductions in low season).

DIRECTIONS The hostel is situated in Cashel town centre, just off the main street, 30 metres along St John Street. Cashel is on the main Dublin to Cork Bus route (N8 road), 155km from Dublin and 90km from Cork.

CRANAGH CASTLE
Templetuohy
Templemore
Co. Tipperary

Cranagh Castle is a Georgian house built onto a medieval tower house. The castle stands in 25 acres of grounds which include a walled garden and an organic farm (home produce and wholefood for sale). We run a rare breeds show and sale in the grounds every September. The castle is a peaceful and spacious house with a music room and lots of books. We have no television and you will need your own sleeping bag or hire sheets for £2 per bed. We are ideal for groups and families (under 12 years half price, small children free). The house is 2km from Templetuohy village which has three good pubs and 6km from bus and train services at Templemore. Please enquire about courses/instruction.

TELEPHONE CONTACT (0504) 53104
OPENING SEASON All Year
OPENING HOURS All day
NUMBER OF BEDS 24
BOOKING REQUIREMENTS Booking is optional, IR£10 deposit secures room.
PRICE PER NIGHT Dorms IR£5, private room IR£7. Sheet hire IR£2 per bed. Under 12 years half price, small children free.

DIRECTIONS The hostel is 2km from Templetuohy which is 6km from buses and trains at Templemore. Leaving Templetuohy take road signposted Thurles and Loughmore, after ½km take small road on the right of a bend. Follow small road for a futher 1½km. Hard to find after dark!

ORMONDE ACCOMMODATION CENTRE

John's Green
Kilkenny
Co Kikenny

The Ormonde Accommodation Centre is located in the heart of Kilkenny, the Medieval capital of Ireland, only two minutes from the bus and train station. This grand historical house is fully refurbished with modern amenities and is approved by the Irish Tourist Board. The Centre consists of single/double/twin rooms and small/large dormitories several with en-suite bathrooms. We offer a wide range of facilities including a self catering kitchen, TV room, conference room, 24 hour reception, luggage store, safe deposit box, private car parking and tourist information. Kilkenny is most famous for its heritage including the restored Kilkenny Castle and St.Canices Cathedral. Kilkenny is also noted for its excellent craft products and craft workshops. The city comes alive at night with superb restaurants, theatres and pubs hosting traditional Irish Music. This is the ideal place in which to relax, meet people and enjoy the *ceol agus craic*!

TELEPHONE/FAX CONTACT Martina (056) 52733 fax 52737
OPENING SEASON All year
OPENING HOURS 24 hours
NUMBER OF BEDS 65
BOOKING REQUIREMENTS Booking advised.
PRICE PER NIGHT IR£7 (large dorm), IR£7.50 (small dorm), IR£9 double room. Group rates negotiable.

DIRECTIONS From the bus/train station turn right and walk two minutes to Wolfe Tone Street, the Ormonde is on the right. Driving from Dublin take N3 then follow signs for Kilkennny.

STUDENT CARE
ACCOMMODATION B&B
114 Lower Baggot Street
Dublin 2
Co Dublin

Student Care Accommodation is a carefully restored Georgian building in the ever popular Baggot Street in central Dublin. Refurbishment of the hostel involved detailed restoration of the ceiling and plasterwork. The hostel has a common room with TV, current reading materials and games. Prices include bed linen, towels and an excellent breakfast.

The hostel is situated in a beautiful tree lined boulevard. It is adjacent to national museums, Trinity College, St Stephens Green, Grafton Street and Temple Bar. Baggot Street is famous for its public houses and restaurants.

TELEPHONE CONTACT (01) 6616516 / 6619860
OPENING SEASON 1st June to 30th Sept
OPENING HOURS 24 hours
NUMBER OF BEDS 50
BOOKING REQUIREMENTS No requirements.
PRICE PER NIGHT £10.50 (dorms), £12.50 (double room) per person. Price include breakfast, towels and all bed linen.

DIRECTIONS Take bus 10 southbound from O'Connell Street (ask for Baggot Street/ Fitzwilliam Street intersection) . Pass Shelbourne Hotel into Baggot Street and on untill you reach the Fitzwilliam Street intersection. The hostel is number 114 on the right hand side of the street (opposite number 41).

MOREHAMPTON HOUSE TOURIST HOSTEL

78 Morehampton Road
Donnybrook, Dublin

Morehampton House Tourist Hostel is a fine Victorian house, with attractive gardens, that has been fully refurbished with modern amenities. Ideally situated in the fashionable Dublin 4 area, the hostel is close to late night shops, good restaurants, pubs and public parks. Conveniently located near to the R.D.S Lansdowne Road Stadium and University College Dublin, it is only a short walk to the city centre. The hostel consists of spacious and comfortable twin/double/triple rooms and small/large dormitories. Several rooms are furnished with en-suite bathrooms. Other facilities on offer include a self-catering kitchen, TV/dining room, 24 hour reception, luggage store, safety deposit box, private car parking and tourist information. Rates include bed linen and free hot showers. Morehampton House provides quality budget accommodation in a relaxed and secure environment - a haven for any traveller.

TELEPHONE/FAX CONTACT Allison/Jordan (01) 6688866 fax 6688794
OPENING SEASON All year
OPENING HOURS 24 hours
NUMBER OF BEDS 69
BOOKING REQUIREMENTS Booking advised.
PRICE PER NIGHT IR£6.95 (large dorm), IR£8.95 (small dorm), IR£11.50 double room. Group rates negotiable.

DIRECTIONS We are on the N11 - signed for Ballsbridge. Buses 10, 46a, 46b from city centre pass our door. From Dun Laoghaire take the 46a bus or the DART to Lansdowne Station.

HOSTEL GUIDES WORLDWIDE

Independent Backpackers Hostels of Scotland. Details of over 60 hostels throughout Scotland from Glasgow and Edinburgh to Orkney and the Western Isles. For a leaflet send a SAE to:- Croft Bunkhouse, 7 Portnalong, Skye, IV47 8SL.

Budget Accommodation in Scotland. Contact M.Campbell, Scottish Tourist Board, 23 Ravelstone Terrace, Edinburgh.

Accommodation for Groups A guide to good value, group accommodation in UK and Ireland. Send £2.95 to: Backpackers Press, 2 Rockview Cottages, Matlock Bath, Derbys, DE4 3PG.

Ireland all the hostels. Available from Bernard Davis, Flat 2a, 72 Woodstock Road, Moseley, Birmingham, B13 9BN.

The 1996 Rambler's Yearbook lists YHA Hostels in the UK and thousands of B&B and self catering houses. Send £5.99 to Ramblers Association, 1/5 Wandsworth Rd, London, SW8 2XX

The CTC (Cyclists' Touring Club) provide worldwide touring information, technical advice, colour magazine and handbook. Contact CTC, Cotterell House, 69 Meadrow, Godalming, Surrey, GU7 3HS. Tel (01483) 417217 Fax 426994

New Zealand Backpackers. Available from Backpackers Resorts of New Zealand Ltd, Box 991 Taupo, New Zealand.

Australian VIP Backpackers Hostels Guide. Write to VIP Resorts, PO Box 1000, Byron Bay, NSW 2481, Australia.

The Hostel Handbook for USA and Canada. This booklet lists over 500 hostels including International YHA Hostels, Independent hostels and unaffiliated sites. Send US$4 (payable Jim Williams) to 722 Saint Nicholas Avenue, New York, USA.

Backpackers Hostels, Canada. For a list of over 70 hostels send 2 postal reply coupons and a self addressed envelope to, Thunder Bay Hostel, RR13, Ontario, Canada

Rucksackers (AAIH) North America Hostel Guide. Write to: 250 West 77th Street, #906, New York, NY 10024, USA